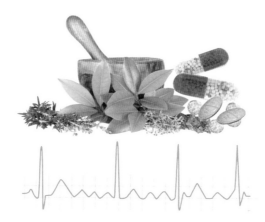

The Islamic Guideline on
MEDICINE

First Edition:2010

Supervised by:

Abdul Malik Mujahid

HEAD OFFICE

P.O. Box: 22743, Riyadh 11416 K.S.A.Tel: 00966-1-4033962/4043432 Fax: 4021659
E-mail: darussalam@awalnet.net.sa, riyadh@dar-us-salam.com Website:www.darussalamksa.com

K.S.A. Darussalam Showrooms:
Riyadh
Olaya branch: Tel 00966-1-4614483 Fax: 4644945
Malaz branch: Tel 00966-1-4735220 Fax: 4735221
Suwaydi branch: Tel: 00966 1 4286641
Suwailam branch: Tel & Fax-1-2860422

- **Jeddah**
  Tel: 00966-2-6879254 Fax: 6336270
- **Madinah**
  Tel: 00966-04- 8234446, 8230038
  Fax: 04-8151121
- **Al-Khobar**
  Tel: 00966-3-8692900 Fax: 8691551
- **Khamis Mushayt**
  Tel & Fax: 00966-072207055
- **Yanbu Al-Bahr** Tel: 0500887341 Fax: 04-3908027
- **Al-Buraida** Tel: 0503417156 Fax: 06-3696124

U.A.E
- **Darussalam, Sharjah U.A.E**
  Tel: 00971-6-5632623 Fax: 5632624
  Sharjah@dar-us-salam.com.

PAKISTAN
- **Darussalam**, 36 B Lower Mall, Lahore
  Tel: 0092-42-724 0024 Fax: 7354072
- **Rahman Market, Ghazni Street,**Urdu Bazar Lahore
  Tel: 0092-42-7120054 Fax: 7320703
- **Karachi,** Tel: 0092-21-4393936 Fax: 4393937
- **Islamabad,** Tel: 0092-51-2500237 Fax: 512281513

U.S.A
- **Darussalam, Houston**
  P.O Box: 79194 Tx 77279
  Tel: 001-713-722 0419 Fax: 001-713-722 0431
  E-mail: houston @dar-us-salam.com
- **Darussalam, New York** 486 Atlantic Ave, Brooklyn
  New York-11217, Tel: 001-718-625 5925
  Fax: 718-625 1511
  E-mail: darussalamny@hotmail.com

U.K
- **Darussalam International Publications Ltd.**
  Leyton Business Centre
  Unit-17, Etloe Road, Leyton, London, E10 7BT
  Tel: 0044 20 8539 4885 Fax:0044 20 8539 4889
  Website: www.darussalam.com
  Email: info@darussalam.com
- **Darussalam International Publications Limited**
  Regents Park Mosque, 146 Park Road
  London NW8 7RG Tel: 0044- 207 725 2246
  Fax: 0044 20 8539 4889

AUSTRALIA
- **Darussalam**-153, Haldon St, Lakemba (Sydney)
  NSW 2195, Australia
  Tel: 0061-2-97407188 Fax: 0061-2-97407199
  Mobile: 0061-414580813 Res: 0061-2-97580190
  Email: abumuaaz@hotmail.com
- **The Islamic Bookstore**
  Ground Floor-165 Haldon Street
  Lakemba, NSW 2195, Australia
  Tel: 0061-2-97584040 Fax: 0061-2-97584030
  Email: info@islamicbookstore.com.au
  Web Site: www.islamicbookstore.com.au

CANADA
- **Nasiruddin Al-Khattab**
  2-3415 Dixie Rd, Unit # 505
  Mississauga
  Ontario L4Y 4J6, Canada
  Tel: 001-416-418 6619

FRANCE
- **Editions & Librairie Essalam**
  135, Bd de Ménilmontant- 75011 Paris
  Tél: 0033-01- 43 38 19 56/ 44 83
  Fax: 0033-01-43 57 44 31
  E-mail: essalam@essalam com-

MALAYSIA
- **Darussalam**
  Int'l Publishing & Distribution SDN BHD
  D-2-12, Setiawangsa 11, Taman Setiawangsa
  54200 Kuala Lumpur
  Tel: 03-42528200 Fax: 03-42529200
  Email: darussalam@streamyx.com
  Website: www.darussalam.com.my

SRI LANKA
- Darul Kitab 6, Nimal Road, Colombo-4
  Tel: 0094 115 358712 Fax: 115-358713

INDIA
- **Islamic Books International**
  54, Tandel Street (North)
  Dongri, Mumbai 4000 09, INDIA
  Tel: 0091-22-2373 4180
  E-mail: ibi@irf.net

SOUTH AFRICA
- **Islamic Da'wah Movement (IDM)**
  48009 Qualbert 4078 Durban,South Africa
  Tel: 0027-31-304-6883 Fax: 0027-31-305-1292
  E-mail: idm@ion.co.za

The Islamic Guideline on
MEDICINE

Yusuf Al-Hajj Ahmad

Translation

Nasiruddin al-Khattab (Canada)

Edited by:

Huda Khattab (Canada)

DARUSSALAM
GLOBAL LEADER IN ISLAMIC BOOKS
Riyadh • Jeddah • Al-Khobar • Sharjah
Lahore • London • Houston • New York

بِسْمِ اللَّهِ الرَّحْمَنِ الرَّحِيمِ

In the Name of Allah,
the Most Gracious, the Most Merciful

© **Maktaba Dar-us-Salam, 2010**
King Fahd National Library Cataloging-in-Publication Data
Ahmad, Yusuf Al Hajj
The Islamic Guideline on Medicine. / Yusuf Al Hajj
Ahmad - Riyadh, 2010
Pages: 285 Size: 17x24 cm
ISBN: 978-603-500-046-8
1-Islam and Medicine. 2- Medicine - Religious
aspects - Islam   I- Title
214.61 dc   1431/8909

L.D. no. 1431/8909
ISBN: 978-603-500-046-8

Contents

Chapter: 7

Chapter: 8

Chapter: 9

Author's Note

All praise is due to Allah. We praise Him and we seek for His assistance and forgiveness. We seek refuge with Him from the evils of our own souls and from our misdeeds. No one can mislead whomever Allah guides and no one can guide whomever Allah causes to go astray.

I testify that there is no deity worthy of worship except Allah. He is One and He has no partner. I also testify that Muhammad is His Slave and Messenger. Allah sent him with the religion of guidance so that it may prevail over all other religions even if the disbelievers dislike that.

Speaking about scientific miracles has become a necessity these days, as knowledge has made great and rapid strides that cannot be stopped even for a moment. Everyday there are new inventions and astounding discoveries. All this strenghtens a Believer's faith and increases confusion in the confused person.

Allah has blessed me with collecting all the conclusions that have been arrived at by the leaders in this art of scientific and medical miracles. I, then, decided that this compilation should comprehensively include every topic relating to miracles either from the Qur'an or from the authentic Sunnah. Some repetitions may be found in this work due to some benefits such as considering the differences in the scholars' methodologies of writing about one topic. The wisdom of this may be found in the popular saying: "You might find in a stream what you might not find in a sea."

Dear reader, on my part I have selected for you the most comprehensive, most authentic, most modern and most beautiful of these proofs. For the purpose of authentication, some of the specialists in these fields have shared their knowledge with me. I would mention, as an example, Dr. Muhammad Harb, a specialist obstetrician and gynecologist and Jihad 'Inayah and Mahir Kabab, who are both pharmacists. I am very grateful to them.

There is no doubt that this work that you are reading, as a first step on what the modern science has arrived at in our contemporary times, has already been mentioned in the Qur'an and mentioned by the Messenger of Allah, peace be upon him, more than 1,400 years ago. This is certainly not going to be the end either. There shall continue to be more and more discoveries that will show humanity that the Qur'an is truly Allah's Word. Allah says about the Qur'an:

$$ \text{﴿ لَّا يَأْتِيهِ ٱلْبَٰطِلُ مِنۢ بَيْنِ يَدَيْهِ وَلَا مِنْ خَلْفِهِۦۖ تَنزِيلٌ مِّنْ حَكِيمٍ حَمِيدٍ ﴾} $$

"Falsehood cannot come to it from before it or behind it; (it is) sent down by the All-Wise, Worthy of all praise (Allah, Glorified and Exalted be He)." (*Soorah Fussilat* 41:42)

He also says:

$$ \text{﴿ وَمَا يَنطِقُ عَنِ ٱلْهَوَىٰٓ ۝ إِنْ هُوَ إِلَّا وَحْىٌ يُوحَىٰ ﴾} $$

"Nor does he speak of (his own) desire. It is only a Revelation revealed." (*Soorah An-Najm* 53:3-4)

This book includes many important topics which are mentioned and discussed. I beseech Allah to cause all that I have collected and written to be a reminder for those who have sound hearts, the ability to listen and have presence of mind, and to make it purely for His sake and to benefit me and the Muslims as a whole with it. Indeed, He has power over all things and He is worthy of accepting prayers. All praise is due to Allah, the Lord of the worlds. May the blessings and peace of Allah be upon our leader Muhammad, his family and his Companions.

Servant of the *Sunnah*

Yusuf Al-Hajj Ahmad

Scientific Miracles in Medicine

Islam promotes medical treatment and urges us not to neglect it, because medical treatment does not conflict with the idea of putting one's trust in Allah, the Exalted. What is forbidden is only treating sickness with impermissible (*Haram*) things, except in cases of acute necessity. According to the *Hadith* which was narrated by Imam Muslim and others, the Prophet, peace and blessings of Allah be upon him, said:

> "For every disease there is a cure; if the right medicine is applied, it will be healed by the leave of Allah."

This *Hadith* indicates that it is prescribed and recommended in Islam to seek medical treatment, and that Allah, the Exalted, has created for every disease a cure. This encourages us to look

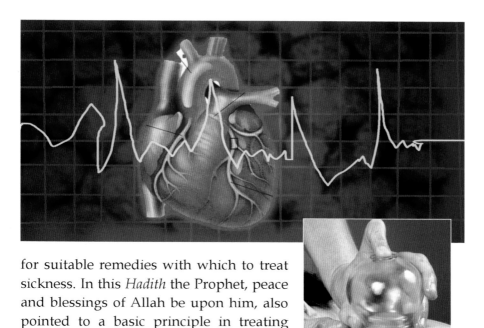

for suitable remedies with which to treat sickness. In this *Hadith* the Prophet, peace and blessings of Allah be upon him, also pointed to a basic principle in treating diseases, which is that the disease must first be diagnosed by specialist doctors, then the proper remedy for that sickness should be prescribed. Undoubtedly, healing depends on correct diagnosis and treatment, by the leave of Allah, Most High. All this depends on the will and decree of Allah. Medical treatment is not contrary to *Tawakkul* (putting one's trust in Allah, the Exalted), just as it is not contradicted by warding off hunger and thirst by eating and drinking, or avoiding that which may lead to sickness and death, and praying for good health and warding off harm.

Medicine in Islam

There are a number of opinions as to what Islamic medicine is. Is it medical knowledge that is completely subject to the will of Allah, or is it the art of treatment adopted and followed by Muslims when the Muslims were at the peak of their development? Or is it the most modern medicine, guided by Divine teachings and completely in accordance with them? Which of these brief definitions is the correct one? We need to lay down some guidelines for the purpose of common understanding. On the basis of Islamic teachings in the Qur'an and *Sunnah,* the following six basic characteristics of Islamic medicine were suggested:

- Adhering to Islamic teachings and etiquette
- Adhering to logic in practicing medicine
- Holistic approach, paying equal attention to the body, mind and soul, for individuals as well as societies
- Universal approach, taking into account all resources and aiming

to benefit all people

- Scientific approach, based on logical conclusions drawn from sound observations, accurate statistics and trustworthy experience

- Excellence, achieving what other kinds of treatment has failed to achieve

These ideas, which were first suggested at the First International Conference on Islamic Medicine held in Kuwait in January 1981, are completely logical although they are theoretical and still unproved. Subsequently, based on these ideas, a program was launched to treat so-called "incurable" diseases, which started in 1986 simultaneously in Panama City, Florida, and Dubai in the United Arab Emirates.

The list of diseases which this program dealt with includes diseases that were regarded as untreatable, such as some cases of advanced cancer (metastatic cancers); chronic degenerative diseases of the bones and joints; diseases of the heart and circulatory system; diseases of the central nervous system; diseases of the liver such as chronic active hepatitis and early chronic cirrhosis; diseases of the respiratory system such as chronic obstructive pulmonary disease; autoimmune diseases such as rheumatoid arthritis, lupus erythematosis, scleroderma, and so on; bronchial asthma and allergies; and, finally, a number of children who were suffering from delays in the developmental milestones of intellectual and physical development, and genetic abnormalities.

These patients all had something in common: they had failed to respond to modern medical treatment, in addition to the fact that some had not been treated at all. The program being mentioned is a Multimodality

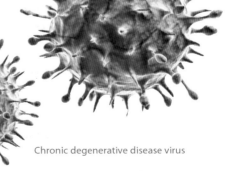

Chronic degenerative disease virus

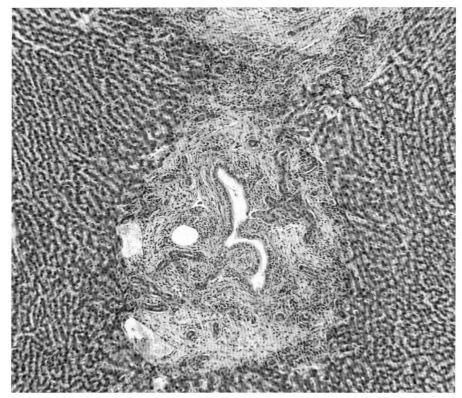

A jumbled mass of cancer forces its way in healthy liver tissue in this microscopic view. 100X

Immunotherapy Program (MIP) which includes a number of alternative modalities or treatment methods, including nutritional programs and a number of nutritional supplements, such as medicinal herbs, vitamins, minerals and enzymes which are administered orally or by injection or intravenously, along with treatment for high temperature, ozone injections, hydrogen peroxide treatment, chelating therapy, ultraviolet light, acupuncture, natural remedies, exercise, and above all emotional rehabilitation, offering advice on how to rid oneself of negative emotions, training in biofeedback, guided imagery and visualization techniques. The cancer patients also received treatment using antigen tumors and some natural products with a selective influence against cancer cells. The program made some fundamental changes in the way the patient eats, thinks and lives, which requires getting rid of all harmful accumulations which may have resulted in lengthy exposure to environmental pollutants and, in brief, living more in harmony with religious teachings and more connected to a healthy lifestyle.

Despite the fact that the program is still in the developmental stage, and is still far from being funded, there have been some results which may seem impossible – according to modern standards of medicine – in the cases of these patients who were not expected to improve at all. They suddenly began to improve, partially or completely, and the ratio of those showing early signs of improvement in the case of non-malignant diseases is 80 percent, and 25 to 30 percent in cases of malignant disease which were thought – until now – to be fatal. At present there are no statistics available on the ratios of recovery, since that requires following up on these patients for at least five to ten years.

Between the onset of a disease that was thought to be untreatable and the end point of full recovery which was thought to be impossible, there is a lengthy road of discovery, one that is filled with new understandings of ancient facts, and new and exciting concepts of health and life. It is very much like walking along a path filled with

Erythrocytes

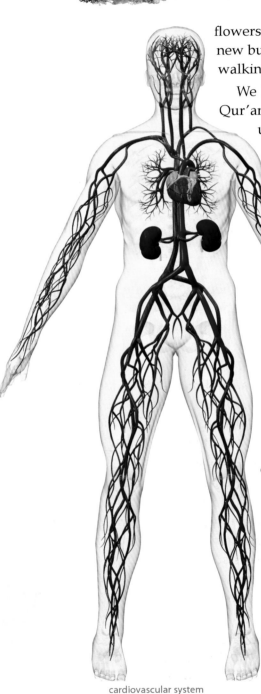

cardiovascular system

flowers, where you can see with your own eyes new buds opening up all around you as you are walking.

We have come to a new understanding of Qur'anic Verses and Prophetic narrations, a new understanding of disease, physiological responses and methods of treatment, and of the connections between chronic disease and autoimmune deficiencies. All the patients who were suffering from chronic diseases, whether benign or malignant, who were seen in Panama City or Dubai, and whose immune systems were assessed, were found to have a certain level of immune deficiency or abnormality, the details of which differed from one patient to another, but it seems that there are certain types of immune abnormality that are more present in certain illnesses or in a certain group of illnesses.

It is understood that there is a connection between chronic disease and negative emotions, as all the patients who suffered from chronic diseases, whether benign or malignant, had a higher level of apparent negative emotions, either before the disease was diagnosed or before the chronic disease manifested itself, and when the chronic disease manifested itself, the negative emotions increased.

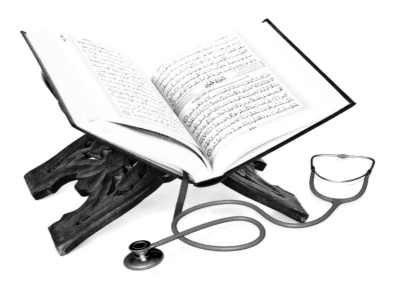

A new understanding of some Qur'anic Verses

We now know from early studies that listening to the Qur'an has a direct impact on lowering stress and an indirect – and possibly direct – impact on stimulating the immune system, which contributes particularly to the healing process. The Qur'anic effect was achieved by listening to the words of Qur'an even without understanding their meaning, but the effect is greater if the words are also understood.

The following studies proved that specific Qur'anic concepts have a great impact in helping the patient to get rid of apparent negative emotions, and in dealing with the negative influences on the immune system that is always present in the case of chronic illness. This healing effect of the Qur'an is clearly apparent in its stimulating effect on the immune system and is used routinely as part of the program with all of our patients, whether they are Muslim or not.

The same may be said of honey in which there is healing for mankind. Our studies and those of others have shown that honey has the effect of stimulating the immune system, in addition to other healing effects. The same may also be said of black seed, in which there is healing for every disease except death. In this phrase there are two mysterious

Honey

points which have not been discussed before:

- Its healing effect for all diseases: Does it help in all kinds of diseases that have different natures and causes?
- The reason why death is excluded from this, because if every person is indeed going to die, does he not need the black seed, or is there some other meaning?

The first mystery was solved when research proved in 1986 and 1987 the stimulating effect of the black seed on the immune system. Hence, it is able to play a role in healing all diseases, during surgery and in reducing post-operative problems. The second mystery was solved at last after many years of observation, because so long as there is still some function or life in the affected tissue or body part, there is still a chance of improvement or healing, whether partial or complete. On the other hand, if the tissue or body part has died completely, and there is a complete loss of function, there is no possible chance of planning or attempting treatment.

Basic features of the effect of multimodality treatment based on Islamic teachings

Various Islamic practices such as fasting, prayer, regular habits, emotional conditioning and some other special elements that are said to have healing effects, such as the Qur'an, honey, black seed and so on, all have something in common, which is that they have a greater effect on chronic internal diseases. Hence, the healing effect is something real and it is not just suppressing symptoms.

The second feature is that the restorative healing effect occurs regardless of the nature of the ailment. This means, for example, that if the number of certain cells is less than it should naturally be, then the treatment leads to an increase in the number of affected cells; if the number of the same cells is greater than what it should naturally be, then the treatment leads to a decrease in the number of affected cells. So the correction, whether upward or downward, restores it only to the natural level, or close to the natural level, and nothing beyond that. This characteristic is usually shared by herbs and all natural remedies, unlike manufactured chemicals which always work in one direction only and increase amounts as the dose is increased, and may go beyond the natural, desirable levels.

It becomes clearer through dealing with chronic diseases that resist treatment, that the physical makeup of a person cannot be separated from his emotional or spiritual makeup. Treatment in s u c h cases cannot be complete unless the restoration treatment is done at the physical, emotional and spiritual levels; failure to correct any abnormality at any of these three levels may reduce the effectiveness of the treatment.

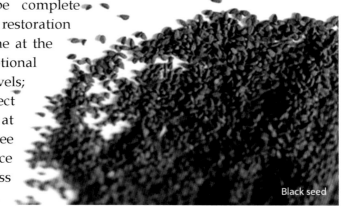

Black seed

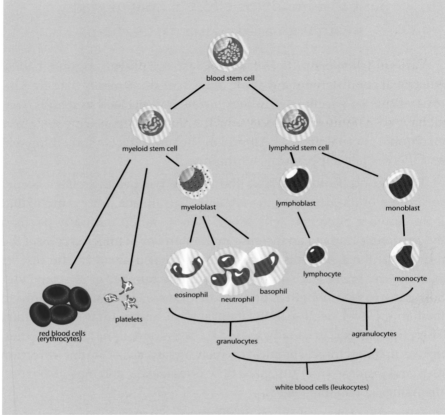

Blood cell

Understanding the interaction with the
immune cells of a particular individual

The immune cells can read a person's mind, record its focus and respond to electromagnetic waves and pulses passing through the mind, i.e., thoughts and feelings. Thus an individual can firmly control the function of the immune cells by controlling his thoughts and emotions. An individual can have an idea about the level of function in the immune cells under the influence of specific feelings by noting the level of performance of things that tip the balance under the influence of the same emotions.

The far-reaching effects of
negative and positive emotions

Purifying the heart of all feelings of resentment and hatred is not just a way to Paradise; it is also a route to better health and better immunity. Similarly, all negative feelings and their positive physiological counterparts may have an effect, positive or negative, on physical health and on an individual's general performance in this world and in the Hereafter.

Comprehensive understanding
of the word contamination

Emotional and mental contamination have a toxic effect on the heart and mind which causes harm commensurate with the degree of chemical and physical contamination in the body. Both of them may have a sufficient effect on the soundness of a person's health and vitality.

We do not know the nature of the soul and how it influences life, but we do know that one aspect of life is the presence of the soul in the body. One aspect of this phenomenon is electricity. So long as there is the exchange of energy going on in the body the person is still alive. When this energy exchange stops at the cellular level that the person is dead. The same thing applies to plants: the living plant, i.e., that which is raw and not cooked or cut up, has a sizeable amount of vital elements, therefore live food has a healing effect or at least a partially healing effect, because the essential elements it contains have a

Human neuron cell

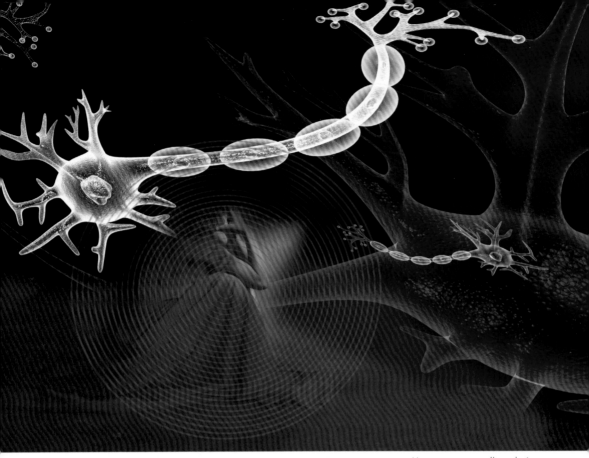

Human neuron cell rendering

positive effect on the human body. As for dead food, it may have some nutritional value, but it does not have a healing effect, because there are no essential elements.

The body is like an electrical machine surrounded by a field of electromagnetic energy, a field of invisible light that is called the aura. This light field may now be seen using electrical imaging (electro photography) or Kirlian photography, then the image may be evaluated. We now know that food and one's emotional state may have a positive or negative effect on a person's aura. On the other hand, the state of the aura may also have a positive or negative effect on the state of the body. Moreover, the aura of one person may affect the aura of another, through physical contact or even physical closeness. This may also be proved by means of electro photography. When we come to understand this mechanism, we will be able to realize the healing effect of positive emotions in children. This can be achieved through parental direction, which may lead to improvement or correction of genetic defects resulting from chromosomal abnormalities without any need for genetic engineering, rather by changing nutritional and environmental factors.

One of the most exciting and puzzling observations that we have seen during the last year is improvement in a number of children who suffer from hereditary problems after using some methods within the framework of the program. We will give some examples:

- There was a five-year-old child who was suffering from milestone delays and it was indeed confirmed that he was suffering from sickness resulting from a chromosome abnormality (10q+10q), which is a case that cannot be treated at all. He could not speak a single word or respond to any commands, but within six months he started responding to commands and saying a few words, and he continued to improve gradually.

- There was a six-year-old girl who was suffering from Thalassaemia major and required monthly blood transfusions, but now she has been receiving treatment for approximately one year, and during the last four months she did not need any blood transfusions at all. A number of other children who were suffering from other hereditary problems have improved to varying degrees. At first these unexpected results could not be explained and it was thought that there were some negative environmental factors which may have had a negative effect on the genetic performance of the cells, as happens in the case of mutation, so perhaps the positive environmental factors led to an improvement. Thus, long-term genetic research was planned in an attempt to explain this situation, so that it could be seen how natural treatment factors affect the reproductive and other genetic factors that lead to chronic diseases.

*****

'O slaves of Allah, Seek Medical Treatment'

It was narrated from Abu Hurairah, may Allah be pleased with him, that the Prophet, peace and blessings of Allah be upon him, said:

"Allah has not sent down any disease but He has also sent down healing for it." (Narrated by Al-Bukhari)

It was narrated from Usamah Ibn Shareek, may Allah be pleased with him, that the Prophet, peace and blessings of Allah be upon him, said:

"Seek medical treatment, for Allah has not created any disease but He has also created a cure for it, except one disease: old age." (Narrated by Ahmad and the four; classed as *saheeh* by At-Tirmidhi)

It was narrated from Jabir, may Allah be pleased with him, that the Prophet, peace and blessings of Allah be upon him, said:

"For every disease there is a remedy, so if you find the right remedy for the disease, you will be healed by the leave of Allah." (Narrated by Muslim)

It was narrated that 'Abdullah, may Allah be pleased with him, said that the Messenger of Allah, peace and blessings of Allah be upon him, said:

"Allah has not sent down any disease but He has also sent down its cure. Those who know it know it and those who do not know it do not know it." (Narrated by Ahmad)

In these narrations there is affirmation and encouragement for medical treatment, and the statement that it is a means of healing, and that medicine is no more than one of the things that Allah, the Exalted, has created as a means of healing and of understanding the nature of things as Allah has created them.

The words "those who know it know it, and those who do not

know it do not know it" encourage Muslim doctors to research and study and discover remedies for diseases that are not yet known and to produce medicines that are better than previous ones. The Prophet's affirmation that for every disease there is a remedy offers strength to the sick person, as it makes him feel that there is a remedy for his disease and that gives him hope and raises his morale, and takes away his fear which is another enemy to him, in addition to his sickness. The Prophet, peace and blessings of Allah be upon him, stipulated that the remedy should suit the disease, so medicines have specific proportions that can be applied, no more and no less.

This encourages Muslim doctors to increase their medical knowledge and skills so that they will be able to apply the remedy in the proper proportions for the disease.

Medical treatment in general is something that is acceptable and encouraged in Islamic teachings. This is proved in the actions and words of the Prophet, peace and blessings of Allah be upon him. If there is any confusion it is due to misunderstanding, for the Messenger of Allah, peace and blessings of Allah be upon him, conveyed the laws of his Lord in word and deed.

As for his words, we have quoted some of them above. Here we will repeat the words of Usamah Ibn Shareek, may Allah be pleased with him, who said, I came to the Prophet, peace and blessings of Allah be upon him, and his Companions, and it was as if there were birds on their heads. I greeted them with Salam, and then I sat down. Then the Bedouins came from here and there, and they said, "O Messenger of Allah, can we seek medical treatment?" He said:

"Seek medical treatment, for Allah has not created any disease but He has also created a remedy for it, except for one disease: old age."

The Prophet, peace and blessings of Allah be upon him, also prescribed several remedies, and we will mention them here to demonstrate that seeking medical treatment is acceptable in Islam and is in accordance with its teachings. For example, the Prophet, peace and blessings of Allah be upon him, sent some doctors to his Companions.

It was narrated that Jabir, may Allah be pleased with him, said that

Cupping Glass

the Messenger of Allah, peace and blessings of Allah be upon him, sent a doctor to Ubayy Ibn Ka'b, may Allah be pleased with him, and he cut a vein and cauterized it. (Narrated by Muslim)

The Prophet's actions are mentioned in many narrations. For example, Al-Bukhari narrated from Ibn 'Abbas, may Allah be pleased with him, that the Messenger of Allah, peace and blessings of Allah be upon him, was treated with cupping on the head for a migraine when he was in *Ihram*.

Imam Muslim narrated from Jabir, may Allah be pleased with him, that Sa'd, may Allah be pleased with him, was struck by an arrow in his medial arm vein, and the Prophet, peace and blessings of Allah be upon him, cauterized it with his own hand, using an arrowhead. It swelled up and he cauterized it again.

These narrations indicate that medical treatment is *Sunnah* and the scholars are unanimously agreed that it is permissible. In fact the general meaning of the command to seek medical treatment indicates that it is more than permissible; at the very least it is *Mustahabb* (recommended).

The Shafi'is are of the view that it is better to seek medical treatment than not to do so. This was also the view of four senior Hanbali *Imams*

(Ibn Al-Jawzi, Abu Ya'la, Ibn 'Aqeel and Ibn Hurairah), who differed from their *Imam*.

Al-Nawawi attributes the view that medical treatment is preferable to the majority of the *Salaf* and most of the later generations.

The Hanafis and Malikis are of the view that medical treatment is permissible, and there is nothing wrong with either seeking medical treatment or not doing so.

Ibn Hanbal was of the view that not seeking medical treatment is preferable, as he said, "Medical treatment is a concession and not seeking it is of a higher level than seeking it." The evidence in his view was the report narrated by Al-Bukhari and Imam Muslim from 'Ata' Ibn Abi Rabah who said, Ibn 'Abbas, may Allah be pleased with him, said to me:

"Shall I not show you a woman who is one of the people of Paradise?" I said, "Yes". He said, "This black woman came to the Prophet, peace and blessings of Allah be upon him, and said, 'I suffer from epilepsy and I become uncovered. Pray to Allah for me.' He said: "If you wish, you can be patient and Paradise will be yours, or if you wish I will pray to Allah to heal you."

She said, "I will be patient." Then she said, "But I become uncovered. Pray to Allah that I will not become uncovered." So he prayed for her.

Al-Bukhari and Muslim narrated that the Prophet, peace and blessings of Allah be upon him, said:

"Seventy thousand of my *Ummah* will enter Paradise without being brought to account. They are the ones who do not seek *Ruqyah* or believe in bad omens, and they put their trust in their Lord."

Al-Kahhal Ibn Turkhan thinks that the Prophet, peace and blessings of Allah be upon him, enjoined seeking medical treatment, and the least that a command can be is recommendation. One of the things that indicate that is the fact

kohl

that the Prophet, peace and blessings of Allah be upon him, continually sought medical treatment when he was healthy and when he was sick. When he was healthy, he did things to maintain his good health, such as exercise, eating little, putting *kohl* on his eyes every night and delaying *Dhuhr* prayer at times when the heat was intense, as he said:

"Wait until it cools down to pray *Dhuhr,* for intense heat is a breeze from Hell." (Agreed upon)

His seeking medical treatment is proved in many narrations, which prove what we have mentioned above about the Messenger of Allah, peace and blessings of Allah be upon him, continually seeking medical treatment both when he was healthy and when he was sick. The Messenger of Allah, peace and blessings of Allah be upon him, did not persist in doing anything but that which is better.

Dr. An-Naseemi affirms, and we agree with him, that the difference of opinion among the *Salaf* with regard to medical treatment is due to the state of medicine at that time, as it was weak and there was a great deal of conjecture.

But if we look at what has been achieved by modern medicine and the narrations that have been narrated about medical treatment, and the fact that the basic teaching of Islam is to protect life and then we can say that medical treatment is subject to five rulings, and Allah, the Exalted, knows best.

- It is permissible if there is no certainty that it is of benefit, as may be said of most cases of cancer, especially if the cancer has spread and was not treated in the initial stages.

- It is *Mandoob* (recommended) to use medicines that are thought most likely to be beneficial, whether that is to heal sickness or reduce symptoms.

- It is obligatory to use medical treatments that are definitely beneficial on the basis of doctors' advice, if the patient or his doctor fears that sickness may prevent him from doing his duties or if he fears for his life or the loss of a limb or faculty.

- It is *Makrooh* (disliked) to use doubtful medical treatments when permissible ones are available.

- It is *Haram* (impermissible) to use *Haram* medical treatment when there is no need to do so.

Based on this, if it is known for sure or thought most likely that the sickness will be healed by using medical treatment and the doctors have determined that the case is serious and that a patient's need for medical treatment is real and is like his need for food and drink, such that not giving it will put his life in danger, then medical treatment is regarded as an obligation under Islamic *Shari'ah* (legislation) and a person is considered as sinning if he does not undergo it.

The Shafi'is, in the person of Imam Al-Baghawi, stated, "If it is known that the medical treatment will lead to healing, then it is obligatory."

Ibn Taymiyah said concerning medical treatment, "In some cases it may be obligatory. That is when he knows that his life can be saved by it and by nothing else, just as it is obligatory to eat dead meat in cases of necessity." It is obligatory according to the four *Imams* and the majority of scholars.

The view that medical treatment is subject to the five rulings was stated by Hujjat Al-Islam Al-Ghazali in *Ihya' 'Uloom Ad-Deen*. It was also regarded as the more correct view by Ibn Taymiyah, when he said in one of his *Fatwas*: "The conclusion is that in some cases it is *Haram*, in some cases it is *Makrooh*, in some cases it is permissible, in some cases it is *Mustahabb* and in some cases it may be obligatory."

Commenting on the types of medicine classified as *Haram*, Al-Baghdadi said: ... Moreover, the problem may be chronic and effectiveness of the medical treatment may be illusionary. The one who takes a poisonous or an unknown medicine is doing wrong, because the Prophet, peace and blessings of Allah be upon him, said:

"Whoever poisons himself, his poison will be in his hand and he will be drinking it in the Fire of Hell." (Agreed upon)

*****

Seeking Medical Treatment and Putting One's Trust in Allah

Seeking medical treatment is not contrary to putting one's trust in Allah, the Exalted, that is *Tawakkul,* which, in fact, is an inclination in the heart when implementing the means that may lead to a desired outcome, because Allah is the One Who does what he wills, and He is the only Healer; the medicine will have no effect without His leave. Based on that, seeking medical treatment is not contrary to putting one's trust in Allah, the Exalted, just as warding off hunger by eating is not contrary to *Tawakkul.* Indeed, true *Tawheed* (Islamic Monotheism) and perfect faith cannot be attained except by implementing the appropriate means that Allah, Most High, has established as the way to attain certain ends, and neglecting the means undermines the very concept of putting one's trust in Allah because that is neglecting the command under *Shari'ah* to seek medical treatment.

Seeking medical treatment is not contrary to belief in *Al-Qadar* (Divine will and decree) either. It was narrated that Abu Khuzamah, may Allah be pleased with him, said that (I said,) "O Messenger of Allah, what do you think of the medical treatment that we seek and the *Ruqyahs* that we ask for and the precautions that we take? Will they protect us against what Allah has decreed?" He said: "They are part of what Allah has decreed." (Narrated by Ahmad, Ibn Majah and At-Tirmidhi, who said: a *saheeh hasan Hadith*)

This narration refutes those who reject medical treatment on the basis of belief in the will and decree of Allah, the Exalted, and the verse in which Allah says:

$$ ﴿ وَإِذَا مَرِضْتُ فَهُوَ يَشْفِينِ ﴾ $$

"And when I am ill, it is He Who cures me." (*Soorah Al-Shu'ara'*, 26:80)

It should be said to such people, "This view of yours implies that you should not implement any of the means that may bring benefit or ward off harm, and this could lead to ruin in your religious and worldly affairs and the spread of mischief in the world. No one could say this but one who stubbornly rejects the truth."

Concerning this, Al-Baghdadi said, implementing the means is part of putting one's trust in Allah, the Almighty. The proficient doctor does what he is supposed to and then he puts his trust in Allah, hoping that He will grant him success and blessings. Similarly, the peasant plows and sows the seeds and then he puts his trust in Allah, the Exalted, hoping that He will make the seeds grow and send rain. Allah says:

$$ ﴿ خُذُواْ حِذْرَكُمْ ﴾ $$

"Take your precautions" (Soorah An-Nisa', 4:71)

And the Prophet, peace and blessings of Allah be upon him, said:

"Tie up your camel and put your trust in Allah." (Narrated by Ahmad and Ibn Hibban)

Imam Al-Ghazali said that with regard to those who did not seek medical treatment or suggested that it should not be sought, as was narrated from Abu Bakr, may Allah be pleased with him, and some of

the *Salaf*, that may be understood in several ways:

- The sick person may have sought medical treatment but it did not benefit him, so he refrained, or else no beneficial treatment was known for his particular problem.

- Or he said what he said, not to reject the idea of medical treatment, but to remind others of the Divine will and decree, or he may have noticed that the people present put too much emphasis on medical treatment and their hearts were not focused on Allah, the Exalted, so his response was like the answer of a wise man or teacher.

- The sick person may have been certain that he was going to die soon.

- It is in one of these ways that we should interpret what was narrated from Abu Bakr, may Allah be pleased with him, when it was said to him, "Why don't we call a doctor for you?" And he said, "The doctor has examined me and said: I shall do as I will."

- The sick person may have been preoccupied with what would happen to him in the Hereafter rather than his situation in the here and now. It was said to Abud-Darda', may Allah be pleased with him, "What is your problem?" He said, "My sins." It was said, "What do you want?" He said, "The forgiveness of my Lord." It was said, "Why don't we call a doctor for you?" He said, *"The doctor made me ill."*

Al-Ghazali interpreted this as meaning that his heart was filled with fear because of his sins and that caused him greater pain than his physical sickness.

Commenting on the narration, "For every disease there is a cure," Imam Al-Nawawi said, This indicates that it is *Mustahabb* to seek medical treatment, and it is a refutation of those who reject medical treatment, such as the extremist Sufis, who claim that everything is subject to the Decree of Allah so there is no need for medical treatment, because medical treatment is also subject to the Decree of Allah, Most High, like *Du'a* (supplication) and fighting the unbelievers.

Medical Treatment
Using Haram Things

It was narrated from Umm Ad-Darda', may Allah be pleased with her, that Abud-Darda', may Allah be pleased with him, said,

"The Messenger of Allah, peace and blessings of Allah be upon him, said:
> "Allah has sent down the disease and the remedy, and He has made a remedy for every disease, so seek medical treatment but do not treat disease with *Haram* things." (Narrated by Abu Dawood and Al-Tabarani; the men of its *Isnad* are *Thiqat* (trustworthy)

Ibn Mas'ood, may Allah be pleased with him, said concerning intoxicants:
> "Allah has not put your healing in that which He has forbidden to you." (Narrated by Al-Bukhari)

It was narrated from Wa'il Al-Hadrami that Tariq Ibn Suwayd Al-Ju'fi asked the Prophet, peace and blessings of Allah be upon him, about *Khamr* (alcohol). He told him not to make it or he disapproved of

him making it. He said, *"We only use it as a remedy"*. The Prophet, peace and blessings of Allah be upon him, said:

"It is not a remedy; rather it is a disease." (Narrated by Muslim)

According to a version narrated by Ahmad: "It is a disease and it is not a remedy."

It was narrated that Abu Hurairah, may Allah be pleased with him, said that the Messenger of Allah, peace and blessings of Allah be upon him, forbade evil remedies. Abu 'Eesa said, meaning poison. (Narrated by Ahmad, Abu Dawood and At-Tirmidhi, who said it is *saheeh*)

Al-Razi said, What is meant by "made for you (*ja'ala lakum*)" is decreed, i.e., prescribed, as in the Verse,

$$﴿ مَا جَعَلَ ٱللَّهُ مِنۢ بَحِيرَةٍ وَلَا سَآئِبَةٍ وَلَا وَصِيلَةٍ وَلَا حَامٍ$$
$$وَلَٰكِنَّ ٱلَّذِينَ كَفَرُواْ يَفْتَرُونَ عَلَى ٱللَّهِ ٱلْكَذِبَ ۖ وَأَكْثَرُهُمْ لَا يَعْقِلُونَ ﴾$$

"Allah has not instituted (ja'ala) things like Baheerah(1) or a Sa'ibah(2) or a Waseelah or a Haam (all these animals were liberated in honor of idols as practiced by pagan Arabs in the pre-Islamic period). But those who disbelieve invent lies against Allah, and most of them have no understanding" (Soorah Al-Ma'idah, 5:103)

What is meant is: He has not prescribed a healing for my *Ummah*, i.e., He has not prescribed his *Ummah* to seek healing, in that which Allah has forbidden to them.

Ibn Al-Atheer said, "*Khamr* is called a disease because of the sin involved in drinking it." The word *Da'* (translated here as disease) is used to refer to faults, defects and bad means. Miserliness is also called *Da'* (a disease).

Ibn Al-Atheer said, evil medicine may be one of two things: First, it may be an impurity (*Najasah*), which is *Haram*, such as *Khamr* and the like, and the flesh, dung and urine of *Haram* animals. All of these are impure and consuming them is *Haram*, apart from what was singled out in the *Sunnah* of camel urine. Secondly, it may be due to its taste, and it is no surprise that this is disliked because people do not like it.

1   (V.5:103) *Baheerah*: A she-camel whose milk was spared for the sake of idols and nobody was allowed to milk it.

2   (V.5:103) *Sa'ibah*: A she-camel let loose for free pasture for their false gods, e.g. idols, and not -ing was allowed to be carried on it.

Ibn Al-Qayyim said, the things that were forbidden to this *Ummah* were forbidden because of their evil as a protection, therefore it is not appropriate to use them as a means of seeking healing from sickness, because even if they have the effect of removing sickness, they may lead to a spiritual problem that is worse because of its inherent evil.

Moreover, if it were permitted to use it for medicinal purposes, especially when people have an inclination toward using that as an excuse to use it for pleasure, and especially when people think it is beneficial and may alleviate sickness – because of all these reasons, the Lawgiver blocked all the possible means that could lead to it being consumed.

The fact that no fair-minded person can doubt is that Allah did not forbid anything to this *Ummah* except that which medicine has proved is extremely harmful and its harm to the body far outweighs any benefits, if there are any. If the *Haram* substance has any healing characteristics that may be useful in some cases, it also has harmful effects that threaten the body's health and outweigh the benefits that may come from consuming it.

Good medicine is that which helps the problem and has few or no side-effects.

Bad medicine, including *Khamr*, is that which modern medicine stopped using as a remedy in the mid-twentieth century and removed completely from the medical vocabulary.

The narrations that we have quoted show that using *Haram* things as medicine is forbidden in *Shari'ah*, and that the Messenger's definitive prohibition of that leads to certainty and the consensus of the *Ummah* on this point. But there are some cases in which the doctor has no other choice but to use *Haram* medicines in order to save his patient from the turmoil of sickness. What is the Islamic ruling in such cases?

Allah says:

﴿ وَمَا لَكُمْ أَلَّا تَأْكُلُوا مِمَّا ذُكِرَ اسْمُ اللَّهِ عَلَيْهِ وَقَدْ فَصَّلَ لَكُم مَّا حَرَّمَ عَلَيْكُمْ إِلَّا مَا اضْطُرِرْتُمْ إِلَيْهِ وَإِنَّ كَثِيرًا لَّيُضِلُّونَ بِأَهْوَائِهِم بِغَيْرِ عِلْمٍ إِنَّ رَبَّكَ هُوَ أَعْلَمُ بِالْمُعْتَدِينَ ﴾

"And why should you not eat of that (meat) on which the Name of Allah has been pronounced (at the time of slaughtering the animal), while He has explained to you in detail what is forbidden to you, except under compulsion of necessity? And surely, many do lead (mankind) astray by their own desires through lack of knowledge. Certainly your Lord knows best the transgressors." (Soorah Al-An'am, 6:119).

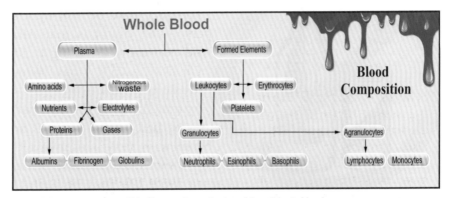

This diagram shows the harmful particles in blood

﴿ حُرِّمَتْ عَلَيْكُمُ الْمَيْتَةُ وَالدَّمُ وَلَحْمُ الْخِنزِيرِ وَمَا أُهِلَّ لِغَيْرِ اللَّهِ بِهِ وَالْمُنْخَنِقَةُ وَالْمَوْقُوذَةُ وَالْمُتَرَدِّيَةُ وَالنَّطِيحَةُ وَمَا أَكَلَ السَّبُعُ إِلَّا مَا ذَكَّيْتُمْ وَمَا ذُبِحَ عَلَى النُّصُبِ وَأَن تَسْتَقْسِمُوا بِالْأَزْلَامِ ذَلِكُمْ فِسْقٌ الْيَوْمَ يَئِسَ الَّذِينَ كَفَرُوا مِن دِينِكُمْ فَلَا تَخْشَوْهُمْ وَاخْشَوْنِ الْيَوْمَ أَكْمَلْتُ لَكُمْ دِينَكُمْ وَأَتْمَمْتُ عَلَيْكُمْ نِعْمَتِي وَرَضِيتُ لَكُمُ الْإِسْلَامَ دِينًا فَمَنِ اضْطُرَّ فِي مَخْمَصَةٍ غَيْرَ مُتَجَانِفٍ لِّإِثْمٍ فَإِنَّ اللَّهَ غَفُورٌ رَّحِيمٌ ﴾

"Forbidden to you (for food) are: Al-Maitah (the dead animals, cattle, beast not slaughtered), blood, the flesh of swine, and that on which the Name of Allah has not been mentioned while slaughtering (that which has been slaughtered as a sacrifice for others than Allah, or has been slaughtered for idols) and that which has been killed by strangling, or by a violent blow, or by a headlong fall, or by the goring

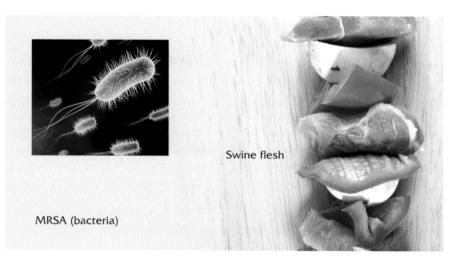

Swine flesh

MRSA (bacteria)

Researchers at the University of Iowa found high prevalence of MRSA (bacteria) swine which may cause serious human infections including skin wounds, breast and heart infections as well as pneumonia.

of horns — and that which has been (partly) eaten by a wild animal — unless you are able to slaughter it (before its death) — and that which is sacrificed (slaughtered) on An-Nusub (stone-altars). (Forbidden) also is to use arrows seeking luck or decision; (all) that is Fisqun (disobedience of Allah and sin). This day, those who disbelieved have given up all hope of your religion; so fear them not, but fear Me. This day, I have perfected your religion for you, completed My Favor upon you, and have chosen for you Islam as your religion. But as for him who is forced by severe hunger, with no inclination to sin (such can eat these above-mentioned meats), then surely, Allah is Oft-Forgiving, Most Merciful." (Soorah Al-Ma'idah, 5:3).

﴿ إِنَّمَا حَرَّمَ عَلَيْكُمُ ٱلْمَيْتَةَ وَٱلدَّمَ وَلَحْمَ ٱلْخِنزِيرِ وَمَا أُهِلَّ بِهِۦ لِغَيْرِ ٱللَّهِ فَمَنِ ٱضْطُرَّ غَيْرَ بَاغٍ وَلَا عَادٍ فَلَآ إِثْمَ عَلَيْهِ إِنَّ ٱللَّهَ غَفُورٌ رَّحِيمٌ ﴾

"He has forbidden you only the Maitah (dead animals), and blood, and the flesh of swine, and that which is slaughtered as a sacrifice for others than Allah (or has been slaughtered for idols, on which the Name of Allah has not been mentioned while slaughtering). But if one is forced by necessity without wilful disobedience for transgressing due limits, then there is no sin on him. Truly, Allah is Oft-Forgiving, Most Merciful." (Soorah Al-Baqarah, 2:173).

These Verses indicate that the All-Wise Lawgiver has exempted cases of necessity from the prohibition, and that He has referred to necessity without any limits, conditions or definitions, which indicates that permissibility is there when there is a necessity, whether it is for the purpose of nourishment in the case of starvation or medical treatment in the case of sickness.

Our scholars have defined necessity as an urgent situation that a person finds himself in facing bad circumstances, that forces him to commit a Haram action in order to save himself from death and ward off unbearable harm, whether on the basis of certainty or probability. Based on that, if the sick person fears for himself or if a Muslim doctor fears for his patient that there may be loss of life or limb, or if his pain has reached an unbearable level, and there is no permissible medicine that can relieve his pain, then it is permissible for him to use or prescribe the forbidden medicine, if a skilled and proficient doctor thinks it most likely that this will benefit him.

The Imams of the Hanafi and Shaf'i schools of jurisprudence are agreed that it is permissible to use Haram medicines in cases of necessity, except intoxicants. Their evidence is as follows:

Allah permitted the pilgrim who is in Ihram for Hajj to shave his head if he is compelled to do so because of an ailment in his scalp, even though shaving the head is one of the things that are forbidden while in Ihram. Allah, the Exalted, says (interpretation of the meaning):

﴾ وَلَا تَحْلِقُوا رُءُوسَكُمْ حَتَّى يَبْلُغَ ٱلْهَدْىُ مَحِلَّهُۥ فَمَن كَانَ مِنكُم مَّرِيضًا أَوْ بِهِۦٓ أَذًى مِّن رَّأْسِهِۦ فَفِدْيَةٌ ﴿

"…and do not shave your heads until the Hady reaches the place of sacrifice. And whosoever of you is ill or has an ailment in his scalp (necessitating shaving), he must pay a Fidyah (ransom) …" (Soorah Al-Baqarah, 2:196)

The Prophet, peace and blessings of Allah be upon him, granted a concession to two of his Companions allowing them to wear silk, which is *Haram* for men, because of an itch that they were suffering. It was narrated from Anas Ibn Malik, may Allah be pleased with him, that the Messenger of Allah, peace and blessings of Allah be upon him, granted a concession to 'Abdur Rahman Ibn 'Awf and Zubair Ibn Al-'Awwam, may Allah be pleased with them, allowing them to wear silk because of an itch that they were suffering. (Narrated by Al-Bukhari and Muslim)

The Prophet, peace and blessings of Allah be upon him, granted a concession allowing gold to be used for medical treatment in the case of necessity to conceal a blemish or remove a deformity. It was narrated that 'Arfajah Ibn Asad, may Allah be pleased with him, said:

Camel's Urine

Ammonia	0.05%
Shulphate	0.18%
Phosphate	0.12%
Chloride	0.6%
Magnesium	0.01%
Calcium	0.015%
Potassium	0.6%
Sodium	0.1%
Creatinine	0.1%
Uric acid	0.03%
Urea	2%
Water	95%

"My nose was cut off during the Battle of Al-Kilab during the *Jahiliyah* period, so I wore a nose of silver, but it caused a foul stench, so the Messenger of Allah, peace and blessings of Allah be upon him, told me to wear a nose of gold." (Narrated and classed as *hasan* by At-Tirmidhi)

The Prophet, peace and blessings of Allah be upon him, granted a concession to a group from 'Uraynah to use camel urine as medicine.

(The *Hadith* is discussed elsewhere in this book).

The Malikis and Hanbalis are of the view that it is not allowed to use *Haram* things for medicinal purposes because of the general meaning of the narration:

> "Allah has sent down the disease and the remedy, and He has made a remedy for every disease, so seek medical treatment but do not treat disease with Haram things."

[Narrated by Abu Dawood and Al-Tabarani; the men of its *Isnad* are *Thiqat* (trustworthy)], regardless of the specific context of the narration because the narration was in a response to a specific question about using intoxicants for medicinal purposes, as was understood by the Hanafis and Malikis.

The majority have agreed that it is *Haram* to use intoxicants for medicinal purposes whether in cases of necessity or otherwise, but the Hanafis made an exception in the case of necessity where healing cannot be achieved except by using intoxicants, based on the general meaning of the Verse:

$$﴿ فَمَنِ اضْطُرَّ غَيْرَ بَاغٍ وَلَا عَادٍ ﴾$$

"But if one is forced by necessity without wilful disobedience nor transgressing due limits." (Soorah Al-Baqarah, 2:173).

An-Nawawi pointed out that the Shaf'i view is that it is forbidden to use *Khamr* for medicinal purposes by drinking it, but what about applying it to the skin as an external remedy in cases of necessity? An-Nawawi allowed that in his book of *Fatwas* called *Al-Masa'il Al-Manthoorah.*

Some Shaf'is limited the prohibition on using *Khamr* as medicine to cases where it is pure and not mixed with anything else in which it is dissolved. If it has dissolved then it is permissible to use it as medicine, subject to the condition that this is done on the advice of a Muslim doctor of good character and that what is used is a small amount that does not cause intoxication (as it says in *Mughni Al-Muhtaj fi Sharh Al-Minhaj* by Al-Sharbeeni Al-Khateeb) or that no taste, color or smell is left (as it says in *I'anah Al-Talibeen*)

The idea of the *Khamr* being dissolved in the medicine means that its structure has been changed by the interaction with the other ingredients of the medicine or that the intoxicating effect has disappeared due to the other ingredients prevailing over it, so that it is impossible to become intoxicated by taking this medicine.

Based on that, in order for it to be permissible to consume medicines that contain alcohol three conditions must be met:

- The sick person should be in need of that medicine due to there being no other permissible medicine that provides equal benefits to those of the medicine that has been prepared with alcohol.

- The medicinal dose should not lead to any initial signs of intoxication.

- A large amount of the medicine should not cause intoxication either, because increasing the dose to that extent leads to damage due to other drugs in the medicine before intoxication takes place. In other words, the effect of the other drugs prevails over the effect of the alcohol, thus alcohol becomes dissolved and absorbed in that medicine.

Based on this, according to the Shaf'is it is not permissible at all to use pure *Khamr* for medicinal purposes or to use what is called medicinal alcohol. With regard to medicine that contains alcohol as an ingredient to make the medicine more palatable or to keep it from going off or to make the medicine easier to dissolve or to distill medicinal essences from plants, it is permissible within the guidelines mentioned above if that is verified by a Muslim doctor of good character.

One example of necessity in which *Haram* things are used for medicinal purposes is the use of drugs in surgery to alleviate unbearable pain, and the use of gold in dentistry and other areas for non-cosmetic treatments, and the use of some hormones derived from pig organs where there is no alternative derived from the organs of cows or other permissible animals, and dealing with cases of hemorrhage by means of blood transfusions, and using organs from dead people for transplant and so on.

Another example is gradual withdrawal from intoxicants in cases where an addict has repented.

Dr. Faisal Al-Sabbagh defined the person who is addicted to alcohol as the one who cannot do without it and cannot go about his daily life without drinking, whereas the moderate drinker is the one who can limit what he consumes, who does not drink regularly and who does not rely on drink to escape painful reality or to cope with anxiety. What is indisputably proved in *Shari'ah* is that the repentance of the one who is not addicted means giving it up completely straight away. But in the case of the addict who has lost his will power because he is so used to it, Dr. Naseemi thinks that if his repentance includes gradually giving up the intoxicant, it is acceptable according to Islam. If he intends to give it up and has even resolved to do so, and he has started gradually to reduce the amount he consumes and to lengthen the time between drinking sessions, it may be good for him because giving it up suddenly without gradually weaning oneself off it under medical supervision may lead to delirium and tremors, and the addict might almost become insane.

He quoted as evidence for that the fact that Islam gradually introduced this prohibition to the *Ummah*. First it was forbidden for a Muslim to come to prayer drunk, so the people began to reduce their drinking so that they would not miss the obligatory prayers, and so on, until those who used to drink a lot rid themselves of their addiction and it became possible to forbid alcohol altogether.

*****

Chapter: 3

A Doctor's Responsibility According to Islam

Imam Malik narrated that the Messenger of Allah, peace and blessings of Allah be upon him, said: "There should be neither harm nor reciprocating harm."

It was narrated from 'Amr Ibn Shu'aib from his father from his grandfather that the Messenger of Allah, peace and blessings of Allah be upon him, said: "The one who practices medicine when he is not known to be a doctor is liable." (Narrated by Abu Dawood and classed as *saheeh* by Al-Hakim and Al-Dhahabi)

Imam Al-Khattabi said, "I do not know of any difference of opinion concerning the practitioner; if he oversteps the mark and the patient dies, he is liable, and the one who practices (medicine) when he has no knowledge of it is a transgressor."

Imam Ibn Rushd Al-Hafeez (Ibn Rushd, the Younger) said, "They are unanimously agreed that if the doctor makes a mistake, he must pay the *Diyah,* such as if he cuts off the tip of the penis during circumcision and the like, because it comes under the heading of offences committed by mistake."

It is superfluous to point out that Islam was ahead of all modern laws in laying the foundation of medical responsibility to protect both the doctor and the patient's rights, and encouraging the development of proper scientific methods in medical procedures.

From the time medicine first emerged in prehistory, it was mixed with magic and myth because the common belief was that sickness resulted from the *Shaitan* taking control of the body, and if a person died, that meant that Satan had overpowered him, so there was no room to find out whether the doctor was responsible.

In Pharaonic Egypt, medical matters were set out in their holy book, and the doctor had to adhere to that. If he went against it and the patient died, the doctor had to give his head as the price (i.e., he was executed).

In Babylon, the Code of Hammurabi included very strict rules which made doctors liable, and the doctor's hand could be cut off if he caused

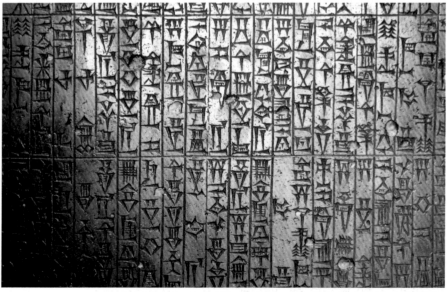

Detail from the Code of Hammurabi stela. Babylonian laws (circa 1760 BC

The Oath

By Hippocrates

I SWEAR by Apollo the physician, and Aesculapius, and Health, and All-heal, and all the gods and goddesses, that, according to my ability and judgment, will keep this Oath and this stipulation- to reckon him who taught me this Art equally dear to me as my parents, to share my substance with him, and relieve his necessities if required; to look upon his offspring in the same footing as my own brothers, and to teach them this art, if they shall wish to learn it, without fee or stipulation; and that by precept, lecture, and every other mode of instruction, I will impart a knowledge of the Art to my own sons, and those of my teachers, and to disciples bound by a stipulation and oath according to the law of medicine, but to none others. I will follow that system of regimen which, according to my ability and judgment, I consider for the benefit of my patients, and abstain from whatever is deleterious and mischievous. I will give no deadly medicine to any one if asked, nor suggest any such counsel; and in like manner I will not give to a woman a pessary to produce abortion. With purity and with holiness I will pass my life and practice my Art. I will not cut persons laboring under the stone, but will leave this to be done by men who are practitioners of this work. Into whatever houses I enter, I will go into them for the benefit of the sick, and will abstain from every voluntary act of mischief and corruption; and, further from the seduction of females or males, of freemen and slaves. Whatever, in connection with my professional practice or not, in connection with it, I see or hear, in the life of men, which ought not to be spoken of abroad, I will not divulge, as reckoning that all such should be kept secret. While I continue to keep this Oath unviolated, may it be granted to me to enjoy life and the practice of the art, respected by all men, in all times! But should I trespass and violate this Oath, may the reverse be my lot!

the loss of any limb or physical faculty of a free man.

In ancient Greece, after Hippocrates rid medicine of a great deal of myth, he forced his students to swear his famous oath, but this oath did not lead to any liability; it was more like a moral or intangible commitment, because there was no criminal liability against the doctor in their view.

In ancient Rome, any mistake or ignorance on the part of the doctor meant that he was required to pay compensation, but the punishment varied according to the social status of the patient. The death of the patient could lead to execution or exile of the doctor.

In mediaeval Europe, if the patient died due to the doctor's negligence or ignorance, he would be handed over

Students then recite the Hippocratic oath

to the patient's family, who would be given the choice between killing him and keeping him as a slave.

Islam ushered in a new era that was governed by just laws revealed by the Allah, when Prophet Muhammad, peace and blessings of Allah be upon him, established the principles that still represent the ideal in regulating the relationship between the doctor and his patient, on the basis of logic and justice. It is worth mentioning that the Muslim jurists regard knowledge of a person's psychology and situation as basic to the science of medicine, as Ibn Al-Qayyim says, "It is essential for the doctor to have knowledge of spiritual and psychological problems, and how to treat them, because that is an important aspect of treating physical matters, because the connection between physical functions and the heart and soul is well known."

If the doctor has knowledge of psychological and spiritual diseases, then he will be the perfect doctor. The one, who has no knowledge of these matters, even if he is very proficient in treating the physical body, is only half a doctor.

Any doctor who does not pay attention to checking the patient's psychological and spiritual state is not really a doctor, rather he is merely pretending to be a doctor.

Because medicine is necessary and is needed by society, Islam regards studying and practicing medicine as a communal obligation. Thus Islam is ahead of manmade laws, because it requires the doctor to put his talents at the service of the community.

The scholar, Muhammad Abu Zahrah, says, "Because of the difficulty in distinguishing the mistakes that cause loss of life or limb, and determining whether they are caused by the doctor's ignorance or negligence, or they resulted from something unforeseen for which no precautions could have been taken, the jurists differed as to whether doctors should be liable to financial penalties in the case of loss of life or limb. Their views are conflicting because this matter may be looked at from two angles, both of which should be heeded.

1. Imposing a financial penalty for the doctor's mistake may lead to doctors refraining from treating sickness if they are not quite sure that their treatment will yield definite results, so that they can avoid penalties. Moreover, many mistakes result from keenness to save lives, so how can a person with that good intention be penalized?

The doctor's work is something that is obligatory according to *Shari'ah*, and the one who makes a mistake while doing an obligatory action should not be questioned about it unless he showed negligence, in which case he is to be taken to task for his negligence, not for his mistake. Negligence and mistakes are two different categories, because the former is a transgression whereas the latter is not.

2. Causing loss of life or limb is a serious matter in and of itself, and it may be the result of the doctor doing something that he is not qualified to do in the hope of earning money, without understanding the consequences. Or he may be qualified to do it but he fell short in examining the patient and the patient or his guardian gave his consent in the hope of recovery, not in order to hasten death. If a person makes a mistake in what he was asked to do and his mistake could have been avoided with due caution and care, he is negligent and the one who is negligent and causes physical harm by his negligence deserves to be punished."

Jurists are unanimously agreed that the ignorant doctor or pretender who deceives people and causes harm should be prevented from practicing medicine.

Imam Ahmad said, "If an unskilled person offers medical treatment, then his action is to be regarded as *Haram.*" They are unanimously agreed that if an ignorant pretender gives the sick person the false impression of having knowledge of medicine, and the patient gives him permission to treat him and dies or is harmed as a result of this treatment, then the doctor is required to pay the *Diyah* or compensation for damages, but we do not say that *Qisas* is required because there was prior consent.

But if the sick person knew that this pretender was not really a doctor, but he still gave himself up to him, then in this case there is no liability because the patient was reckless and was not deceived.

Abu Zahrah said, "Here we are speaking of the harm that could befall the patient, and that which may be done by a skilled doctor or may result from his treatment. Concerning this case, the jurists are divided and there are four points of view:

1. That the patient's loss of life or limb is due to something that was unforeseeable and the doctor, despite his skill and precautions, could not have foreseen it. This was not due to a mistake or negligence on the part of the doctor, so in this case there was no shortcoming or negligence for which the doctor should be made liable. The jurists are unanimously agreed that if death or harm came about because of doing an obligatory action while taking precautions and not being negligent, then there is no liability, as in the case of the one who dies when carrying

out a *Hadd* punishment that is in accordance with *Shari'ah*, because that is done by way of carrying out a religious duty and not by negligence which may be regarded as a transgression that dictates liability or by mistake which may be regarded as killing a man in error for which there should be *Diyah*, because if liability is dictated in this case, that would be an obstacle to doctors doing their duty.

2.   That harm has been caused to the limb or body because of a procedural mistake on the part of the doctor, such as when a surgeon takes all precautions but his hand slips and damages all of part of the body. No doubt there should be liability in this case, because if he damages the entire body in a way that causes it to die, he will be regarded as having killed in error. In the *Madhhab* of Ibn Hanbal there is a difference of opinion: Should the *Diyah* be paid by the public treasury (*Bait Al-Mal*) or from the doctor's wealth? The evidence of those who say that it should be paid from the doctor's wealth is that the basic principle is that it should be paid by his *'Aqilah* (i.e., his male relatives on the father's side), and if he does not have an *'Aqilah* then it should be paid from his own wealth.

As for the report which says that it should be paid from the *Bait Al-Mal*, this is based on the assumption that the doctor's error is like the error of a judge, because they were appointed by the ruler for the benefit of the public, so he is liable for their mistakes which are not due to any shortcomings on their part, but happened because they were overtaken by the decree of Allah, the Exalted, with regard to what they do.

3.   If death occurs due to prescription of the wrong remedy, although the doctor strives hard and does his best, but like anyone who strives to work out the right answer, he may be right or wrong, and his mistake leads to the death of a human soul, then in this case he should definitely be liable, and the *Diyah* should be paid as in the case of killing by mistake. There are also two reports from Ibn Hanbal, one of which says that the *Diyah* should be paid by the *'Aqilah* of the doctor and the other says that it should be paid by the public.

4.   In the first three categories, medical treatment was given with permission of the patient or his guardian. But if the mistake or negligence

in any of the forms described above occurred without the permission of the patient or his guardian, then the jurists are unanimously agreed that liability is *definite*, because this action led to loss of life or limb without the guardian's permission, so he (the doctor) is responsible for it, and the liability is to be borne by his *'Aqilah*.

Ibn Al-Qayyim favored the view that the doctor is not liable in this case, and he probably thought that liability was to be borne by the public treasury. He justified that by saying, "It may be that he is not liable at all, because he was doing an act of kindness and no ground (of complaint) can there be against the *Muhsinoon* (good-doers) (cf. *Soorah Al-Tawbah* 9:91). Moreover, if he was transgressing then the guardian's consent is irrelevant with regard to waiving liability, and if he was not transgressing then there is no liability. If you say that he was transgressing when there was no consent, and he was not transgressing when there was consent, I say: The issue of whether he was transgressing or not has to do with his action, and it does not matter whether there was consent or not."

This phrase leads us to conclude that Ibn Al-Qayyim did not think that the skilled doctor is culpable if he does his job in the proper manner, but then something unexpected happens or the Divine decree overtakes him and his hand slips or he makes a mistake in prescribing the remedy; it makes no difference whether the treatment was given with or without the permission of the patient or his guardian or anybody, because when there is consent, then he has authority, and if there is no consent

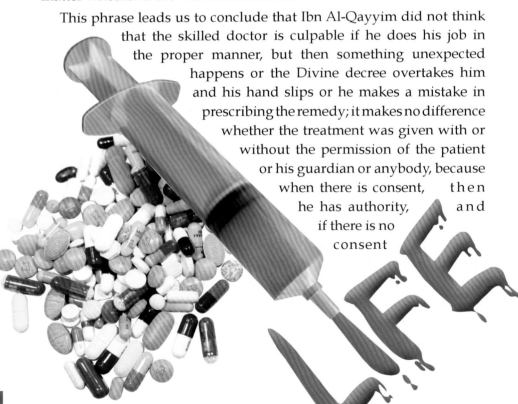

then he is doing a charitable deed and a religious duty, so there is no liability.

Liability has to do with whether the action was done properly or not; so long as he has done his work in the proper manner or he has done his best, as any qualified doctor would do, then there is no liability to be borne by him or his 'Aqilah.

♦ Abu Zahrah supported the view of Ibn Al-Qayyim but he favored the idea that liability was to be paid by the public treasury of the Muslims so that Muslim lives would not be lost in vain. The Qur'an clearly states that the lives of Muslims should not be taken in vain even if it is by mistake:

﴿ وَمَا كَانَ لِمُؤۡمِنٍ أَن يَقۡتُلَ مُؤۡمِنًا إِلَّا خَطَـًٔا وَمَن قَتَلَ مُؤۡمِنًا خَطَـًٔا فَتَحۡرِيرُ رَقَبَةٍ مُّؤۡمِنَةٍ وَدِيَةٌ مُّسَلَّمَةٌ إِلَىٰٓ أَهۡلِهِۦٓ إِلَّآ أَن يَصَّدَّقُواْ ﴾

"It is not for a Believer to kill a Believer except (that it be) by mistake; and whosoever kills a Believer by mistake, (it is ordained that) he must set free a believing slave and compensation (blood money, i.e. Diyah) be given to the deceased's family unless they remit it …" (Soorah An-Nisa', 4:92)

Part of encouraging the practice and profession of medicine is that liability is not paid from the doctor's wealth; rather, it is paid from the public treasury of the Muslims. Thus we will have reconciled between the Qur'anic text and encouragement to do research and treat sickness.

There are ten cases in which medical liability is confirmed in *Shari'ah*:

• Deliberate intent

This means that the doctor did something disallowed that led to the death of the patient or destruction of one of his limbs or bodily functions, and his aim in doing so was to harm and hurt the patient, such as if he prescribed poisonous medicine for him with the aim of killing him. This is to be regarded as a deliberate killing for which *Qisas* is required. This is rarely done by doctors.

- Error

Such as if the doctor makes a mistake in his diagnosis of the sickness and then prescribes the wrong medicine or thinks that there is a need for surgery, then it becomes clear after doing surgery that the patient did not need it, or the surgeon's hand slips when doing surgery. Undoubtedly the doctor is responsible for his mistake and for the harm that results from that mistake, responsibility for the mistake is less serious than responsibility for a deliberate action, because there was no intention of deliberate transgression on the part of the one who made this mistake, therefore this case differs from the case of deliberate intent in that there is no *Qisas*, even though in both cases there is liability. Moreover, even if there is liability in worldly terms that is connected to this error, the person is not sinning before Allah, the Exalted.

- Doing something contrary
  to the principles of medicine

When a doctor treats a patient in a manner contrary to the established principles of medicine, his deed changes from one that is proper and encouraged to one that is *Haram*, for which he may be punished. The jurists explained that following the established principles of the profession is regarded as obligatory for the doctor. Therefore, he is liable for any harm that results from going against this duty.

- Ignorance

Such as when an imposter claims to be practicing medicine but he is deceiving and cheating the patient by claiming to have knowledge, or it may be that he has some basic knowledge but it does not qualify him to practice this profession, such as a medical student for example; or he has some knowledge of one branch of medicine, but he decides to work in a different specialty.

In all of these cases, the imposter is regarded as liable, because the jurists are unanimously agreed that the ignorant doctor should be made liable for the harm he causes by his ignorance and his deceit of the patient. We have quoted above the narration: "The one who practices medicine when he is not known to be a doctor is liable."

- ## Absence of consent from the patient

What Allah, Most High, has blessed man with of organs and faculties are regarded as his right and it is not permissible for anyone else to dispose of them without his permission. On this basis, it is not permissible for the doctor or anyone else to handle a person's body for the purpose of examination, treatment or surgery, until after he has got permission from the patient or his guardian if he is not qualified to give permission, such as a minor or one who is insane or unconscious.

The majority of scholars in the four schools of Islamic jurisprudence are of the view that liability cannot be waived from the doctor who gives treatment without the patient's permission. In *Al-Fatawa Al-Hindiyah*, it says "if it is done without permission then he is liable, whether he transgressed or not." Ibn Al-Qayyim and Ibn Hazm disagreed with that and said that there is no liability except in cases of error.

- ## Absence of license from the authorities

This refers to the ruler who is in charge of the nation's affairs, who is represented nowadays by the ministry of health which gives permission to practice medicine. Based on that, the doctor is considered liable if he did not try to obtain this permission or license. But the permission of the ruler does not mean that liability is waived from the doctor if he is not qualified.

- ## Deceit

This means cheating. The doctor is regarded as cheating and deceiving if he prescribes medicine for the patient that is harmful or that he cannot bear, or that is of no benefit in his particular case, but the patient takes it because he has been deceived by the doctor. The doctor is regarded as liable for the harm that results from his deception of the patient.

- ## Doctor's refusal to offer treatment in emergency situations

In *Al-Taj Wal-Ikleel*, which is a Maliki book, it says, "it is obligatory for everyone who fears that a Muslim may die to help him in whatever way

he can." Muhammad Abu Zahrah narrated that there was consensus that whoever has extra food in the wilderness and sees before him a person who is starving is sinning if he leaves him to die.

A case where a sick person is about to die is like the case of the starving man in the wilderness, so helping him is regarded as something obligatory according to the majority of jurists. Based on that, it is the sick person's right that the doctor should be forced to help him, if the doctor is able to do so and the sick person is in urgent need.

- ## *Haram* remedies

It is not permissible for man to expose his faculties to destruction and ruin until he meets Allah on the Day of Resurrection. Just as the sick person has no right to do that, his permission to the doctor to kill him or damage him does not make it permissible for the doctor to do anything of that nature or tamper with him. Islam does not permit the sick person to give his consent for that, and it does not give his consent any weight in waiving liability from the doctor if he goes ahead and kills the patient, even if his motive is compassion.

- ## Disclosing the patient's secret

The nature of the doctor's work involves dealing with the patient's body in general and seeing their *'Awrahs* (private parts) and matters that are private to the patient that no one else should know about. Were it not for the hardship of sickness and the severity of pain, the sick person would not disclose any of his personal matters to the doctor. So the doctor must respect this trust that his patient has given to him.

﴿ وَٱلَّذِينَ هُمْ لِأَمَٰنَٰتِهِمْ وَعَهْدِهِمْ رَٰعُونَ ﴾

"Those who are faithfully true to their Amanat (all the duties which Allah has ordained, honesty, moral responsibility and trusts) and to their covenants." (Soorah Al-Mu'minoon, 23:8)

Moreover, disclosing the patient's secret, with the harm that it involves, is undoubtedly *Haram*. In the event that no harm is involved, even if it is not *Haram*, it is still disliked. The harm that may befall the patient makes the doctor liable if he discloses his secrets.

No exception is made except what is required in cases of necessity in the public interest, such as if the doctor knows that, for example, his patient who is a pilot suffers from epilepsy, a condition which means that he should not fly planes and put people's lives in danger; he must disclose the matter and not conceal it. Of course, the degree of necessity must be evaluated properly and he should not disclose more than is necessary.

To sum up, the qualified doctor is not responsible for harm that may befall his patient if the following conditions are met:

1. Proved medical knowledge

2. Permission or license from the authorities

3. Consent of the patient or his guardian

4. Working in accordance with the well-established principles of medicine

5. Not making a serious mistake which incurs liability.

All of this is based on the assumption that the doctor is proficient and does not fall short or neglect the care of his patient. But in fact we see that a doctor may fall short or not try hard, even when a human life has been entrusted to his care. This happens a great deal in public hospitals which are used by the poor. You see many doctors being careless and

failing to help the patients, which leads to complaints from the patients and those whose souls go to their Lord complaining of the wrongdoing and negligence of these doctors.

It may also happen in private clinics where a doctor has too many patients, so he has a quick look and quickly writes a prescription, which may hasten the patient's death.

All the principles of *Fiqh* (Islamic jurisprudence) indicate that such doctors are liable because their negligence is regarded as a transgression against people's lives, so liability is due to their negligence. Jurists are unanimously agreed that liability is due in cases of transgression, and they are unanimously agreed that negligence is a form of transgression. There can be no escape from the punishment of Allah, the Exalted, in the Hereafter after the punishment in this world, and Allah will take care of the sinners and punish them for their transgressions and negligence, as He will take care of the doers of good for their good actions.

*****

Ethics And Etiquette
Followed By Doctors In Islam

From the point of view of *Shari'ah*, the doctor must possess a number of attributes in order to be qualified to carry out his medical duties in a proper manner. Even though fulfilling this mission is a communal obligation, Muslim scholars have regarded it as one of the noblest of professions because it has to do with preserving life and helping man to perform his duties as vicegerent on this Earth. However, scholars have stipulated two conditions with regard to medical practitioners:

1.   He should practice the profession with proficiency and sincerity.

2.   The doctor should pay attention to developing the proper Islamic attitude.

Dr. Shawkat Al-Shatti compiled the requisite attributes of a skilled doctor that are required in Islam from a number of writings on Islamic medicine. They are as follows:

- The doctor should try to establish the causes of sickness and the circumstances that lead to it, which includes identifying the type of sickness, the manner of its onset and the reasons that caused it.

- He should pay attention to the patient, his physical strength and changes in his body and habits.

- The doctor's aim should not only be to deal with the problem but to remove it in such a way that will not lead to another problem that is worse. However, if there is no guarantee that removing it will not lead to another possibly worse problem, it should be left as it is and the symptoms should be treated.

- The doctor should deal with the disease first by adopting the easiest method and then the next easiest. He should not move from treating the disease with food to treating it with medicine unless he has no choice, and he should not move to complicated remedies unless he cannot use simple remedies.

- He should look at the strength of the medicine and weigh it up in relation to the strength of the disease.

- He should look at the problem and see whether it is something that can be treated or not. If it cannot be treated then he should preserve the dignity of his profession and his own dignity, and not let greed push him to treat something that is untreatable.

- He should have experience in dealing with emotional and psychological problems and their remedies, because this is an important part of treating physical problems, because the physical nature of the body and the way it affects the psyche is well known.

- He should be kind and gentle toward the patient.

- He should use methods such as imagery; a proficient doctor may achieve by these means that which could not be achieved by means of medicine.

- The doctor should give treatment with the aim of achieving six things: Preservation of existing health, restoration of lost health, removal or reduction of the problem, putting up with a less serious problem in order to remove the worse, and foregoing the lesser of two benefits in order to achieve the greater.

What is meant by imagery is instilling good images (positive imagery), which remind us of the importance of treating the patient well and reassuring him, which is essential in order to support the immune system in the body.

Al-Taj Al-Subki, may Allah have Mercy on him, summed up the etiquette of the doctor as follows:

It is his duty to be sincere and kind toward the patient. If he sees the signs of death, it is not a bad idea to remind him to make a will with subtle words. It is permissible for him to see the 'Awrahs (private parts) if necessary, but only as much as is necessary. Most mistakes made by doctors are due to not understanding the real nature of the

sickness and rushing to prescribe treatment, and not understanding the patient's psychology or starting to practice medicine without being fully qualified. He should understand that his medicine will not change the Divine will or decree, and that he is practicing medicine in obedience to the command in *Shari'ah* and on the basis that Allah, the Exalted, has sent down both the disease and the remedy.

Abu Bakr Al-Razi affirmed this point in his discussion of the doctor's attitude, and said, when treating sickness, the doctor should put his trust in Allah and hope for a cure from Him, not because of his own sagacity and proficiency. He should rely on Allah in all his affairs. If his attitude is the opposite, and he focuses on himself and his own proficiency and skill, then Allah, the Almighty, may deprive him of results.

A doctor practicing his profession properly comes under the general meaning of the words of the Prophet, peace and blessings of Allah be upon him: "Allah loves when one of you does a thing, so do it well." (Narrated by Al-Baihaqi)

And it is what we understand from the words of the Prophet, peace and blessings of Allah be upon him: "Allah has not sent down any disease but He has also sent down its cure. Those who know it know it and those who do not know it do not know it." (Narrated by Ahmad)

This *Hadith* is an encouragement to research and discover effective medicine; it encourages the doctor to increase his medical knowledge and be proficient, because the correct remedy will lead to healing, as we understand from the words of the Prophet, peace and blessings of Allah be upon him: "If the right remedy is applied, (the patient) will be healed by the leave of Allah." (Narrated by Ahmad)

The Messenger of Allah, peace and blessings of Allah be upon him, taught us that help should be sought in any field or profession from the person who is most proficient in it, because the one who is more proficient is more likely to attain results.

In *Al-Mu'watta'*, Imam Malik, may Allah have Mercy upon him, narrated from Zaid Ibn Aslam that one of the Companions of the Messenger of Allah, peace and blessings of Allah be upon him, was wounded and the wound started bleeding. He called two men of *Ansar* and the Messenger of Allah, peace and blessings of Allah be upon him, said: "Which of you has more knowledge of medicine?" One of them said, "Is there any good in medicine, O Messenger of Allah?" He said: "The One Who sent down the disease is the One Who sends down the cure."

[The *Hadith* is *mursal* (a narration where the chain of narrators is cut off), and is from Zaid Ibn Aslam who was one of the senior *Tabi'een* (followers), and his *mursal* reports are *saheeh* according to the *Muhadditheen* (*Hadith* scholars).

The *Hadith* was also narrated by 'Abd Al-Malik Ibn Habeeb, in his book *Al-Tibb Al-Nabawi*, from the companions of Malik whom he met in Madinah. In his report he added, one of them said, "I have more knowledge of medicine," and the Messenger of Allah, peace and blessings of Allah be upon him, ordered him to treat him, so he opened his stomach and took out a metal arrowhead, then he stitched it up.

Rushing to relieve the distress of the patient is fulfilling the duty of helping him by night and day, which is one of the duties of a Muslim doctor, because the Messenger of Allah, peace and blessings of Allah be upon him, said: "Whoever relieves a Muslim of some distress in this world, Allah will relieve him of some distress on the Day of Resurrection. Whoever is easy-going with a debtor who is facing hardship, Allah will make it easy for him in this world and in the Hereafter. And whoever conceals a Muslim's faults, Allah will conceal his faults in this world and the Hereafter. And Allah will help His slave so long as His slave helps his brother." (Narrated by Muslim)

The doctor should start his treatment, surgery or prescription

by saying *Bismillah* (in the Name of Allah) or *Bismillah il-Rahman il-Raheem* (in the Name of Allah, Most Gracious, Most Merciful), because the Prophet, peace and blessings of Allah be upon him, said: "Any important words or actions that do not start with mention of Allah will be defective." (Narrated by Ahmad, Abu Dawood, Ibn Majah; it is a *hasan Hadith* when all its *Isnads* (chains of narrations) are taken into consideration)

The doctor's duties include: offering sound advice and intending by his actions to benefit people and be kind to them. Sincerity toward the patient includes prescribing the most suitable medicine for him and preserving his wealth, so he does not prescribe for him any medicine that will not help with his sickness, or ask him to undergo tests and examinations just so that he (the doctor) or the lab with which he works and from which he gets commission can benefit. All of these actions are a betrayal of the patient and breaking the trust enjoined on the doctor who is required to be sincere toward the patient.

The Prophet, peace and blessings of Allah be upon him, said: "Your blood, your wealth and your honor are sacred to you, as sacred as this day of yours in this month of yours. Let those who are present among you convey it to those who are absent." (Agreed upon)

That includes protecting the honor of the patient and not uncovering any of his *'Awrah* except that which is necessary in order to complete the medical examination.

Sincerity toward the patient also means not treating him if he (the doctor) is not in the right mood; so he should not treat him if he is upset or in a hurry or angry. The scholars drew an analogy for doctors based on the *saheeh* report in which the Prophet, peace and blessings of Allah be upon him, forbade judges to pass judgment when angry. (Agreed upon)

In such cases a man will be unable to judge matters properly. An exception is made in cases where a person needs to be treated urgently.

Sincerity toward the patient also means spending enough time with him and his family to examine him and to understand the social and spiritual situation of the patient, who is composed of body, mind and soul. The doctor should touch him gently, speak to him in a humane and compassionate manner, listen to him carefully, calm him down and try to comfort him; this may increase the patient's resolve, raise his spirits and strengthen his immune system – these are all factors that aid in healing.

The doctor should not hesitate to send his patient to a specialist or a consultation committee if the situation calls for that, as part of the trust and sincere advice that are required of him by *Shari'ah*. He should avoid backbiting people or criticizing them, especially his fellow doctors.

The doctor is obliged to conceal his patient's secrets because the Prophet, peace and blessings of Allah be upon him, said: "The one who is consulted is entrusted with a secret." (*Saheeh* – it was narrated by the authors of *Al-Sunan*)

However, he may disclose the secret if it is in the interests of the patient or in the interests of the community.

Abu Bakr Al-Razi said, "Know, O my son, that the doctor should be kind to people and avoid talking about them in their absence; he should conceal their secrets because some people may have a sickness that they want to conceal even from the closest of people to them, and what they conceal is something private that they have disclosed to the doctor only out of necessity. If he treats one of his womenfolk or female slaves, he should lower his gaze and not look beyond the site of the problem."

The doctor must have knowledge of *Halal* and *Haram* with regard to his profession, and he should not prescribe any *Haram* remedy unless there is no other cure, because the Prophet, peace and blessings of Allah be upon him, said: "Do not treat (sickness) with *Haram* things."

And Allah, the Exalted, says:

$$﴿ وَقَدْ فَصَّلَ لَكُم مَّا حَرَّمَ عَلَيْكُمْ إِلَّا مَا اضْطُرِرْتُمْ إِلَيْهِ ﴾$$

"He has explained to you in detail what is forbidden to you, except under compulsion of necessity." (Soorah Al-An'am, 6:119)

We have explained this in detail in our discussion on using *Haram* things as medicine.

The prohibition on employing *Haram* means of treatment includes refusing to perform abortions or to end the life of a terminally sick patient, no matter what the means, because Allah says:

$$﴿ وَلَا تَقْتُلُوٓاْ أَنفُسَكُمْۚ إِنَّ ٱللَّهَ كَانَ بِكُمْ رَحِيمًا ﴾$$

"And do not kill yourselves (nor kill one another). Surely, Allah is Most Merciful to you." (Soorah An-Nisa', 4:29)

Rather, he should try to reduce the pain, and comfort the patient until his time comes.

The doctor's knowledge of *Halal* and *Haram* and his proficiency in medicine should make him fear Allah, Most High, when advising his patients; he should not advise a patient not to fast in Ramadan if he knows that the patient will not be affected by fasting and may benefit from it.

Part of the doctor's etiquette is to pray for his patient and offer him consolation, such as saying, "May Allah heal you" or saying any supplication narrated in *Hadith*.

It was narrated from Anas, may Allah be pleased with him, that the Prophet, peace and blessings of Allah be upon him, entered upon a Bedouin to visit him when he was sick with a fever. He said: "There is no harm to you, it is purification if Allah wills." (Narrated by Al-Bukhari)

His praying for the patient is a reminder to him of the Creator of the disease and the cure, so he will remain calm and will turn to Allah, the Almighty, and put his trust in Him.

Doctors vary in the treatments they offer to patients who have no hope of a cure, such as those who have cancer. Some give them the hope of recovery but they may be lying. And some tell the truth frankly, and some try to be gentle and speak in ambiguous terms. What is the Islamic view on that?

According to Dr. Al-Naseemi, the doctor should be tactful when informing the patient about his disease; he should try to comfort him and raise his morale, and not tell him that his life is in danger, rather he should tell his next-of-kin, based on the report narrated by Abu

Sa'eed Al-Khudri, may Allah be pleased with him, according to which the Prophet, peace and blessings of Allah be upon him, said: "When you enter upon a sick person, try to reassure him that he is going to live; that will not change anything but it will comfort him." Abu 'Eesa said, "This is a *ghareeb Hadith*." (Narrated by At-Tirmidhi, Ibn Majah; its *Isnad* includes Ibrahim Al-Tameemi who is *munkar al-Hadith*)

Dr. Zuhair Al-Saba'i says that Islam does not give precise guidelines in such cases, and does not take a rigid stance. Rather, it expects the doctor to exercise good judgment and deal with each case on its own merits:

- There are some patients who may collapse if they know the true nature of their sickness.

- There are strong believers who can confront and accept their sickness.

- There are some who need to know the extent of the problem so that they can adhere to a treatment regime.

The basic principle that is set out by Islam is that one should tell the truth, but what truth are we talking about? Does the doctor know when the patient's life is going to end? Rather, truth means explaining the extent of the problem, not estimating how much time the patient has left. There is truthfulness that is blunt and insensitive and pays no attention to the patient's feelings, and there is truthfulness that is based on wisdom and compassion. It may be wise for the doctor to speak frankly to his patient but in general terms, not in details. If there are real complications, then he has to explain them to the family of the patient so that he will not be accused of negligence.

Qais Aal Al-Sheikh Mubarak is of the opinion that if the patient cannot take care of himself or is too young, then he should not be told, because such a person is not in charge of himself, but the doctor should tell his guardian who gave permission to treat him, because a child is likely to get upset.

In the case of an adult of sound mind, *Shari'ah* dictates that he should be told everything that has to do with his health; this obligation is based on the contract between them.

Then he said, "If the doctor fears that the position of the patient may get worse if he knows the truth, this is not grounds for not telling him, for two reasons:

- The doctor has committed himself to that according to the contract and it is not permissible for him to break the contract.

- Belief in the Divine will and decree protects a Muslim from falling into confusion and despair; the Muslim is enjoined to be patient and submit to the decree of Allah, the Exalted.

But Qais Ibn Muhammad revisited the issue and said, "However, when the doctor realizes that it is not possible to tell his patient, it is permissible for him to tell his family and relatives so that they can take on the mission of telling him, but he should choose suitable phrases, as Imam Al-Subki said, 'If he sees the signs of death, it is not a bad idea to remind him to make a will with subtle words'."

Part of the doctor's etiquette is to look well-dressed; his clothes should be comely, clean and appropriate to the position that Allah has put him in.

He should also take care of his own health, because if he is not healthy, his patients will not trust him and will be put off.

✳✳✳✳✳

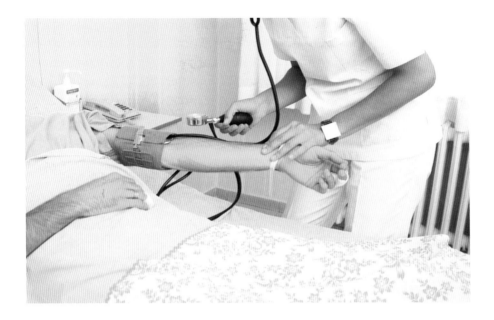

One Gender Treating The Other

It was narrated that Al-Rubayyi' Bint Mu'awwith, may Allah be pleased with her, said, "We were with the Prophet, peace and blessings of Allah be upon him, bringing water, treating the wounded and bringing the slain back to Madinah." (Narrated by Al-Bukhari)

Ibn Hajar, may Allah have Mercy upon him said, "This *Hadith* indicates that it is permissible for a non-*Mahram* (marriageable) woman to treat men in cases of necessity. He said in the chapter on *Men Treating Women and Women Treating Men*: With regard to the ruling on this issue, it is permissible to treat non-*Mahrams* in cases of necessity, but that should be properly guarded with regard to looking, touching and so on."

This indicates that women may treat men; so, by analogy men may treat women.

For every military campaign the Prophet, peace and blessings of Allah be upon him, would draw lots among his wives and the one who was chosen would go out with him. The female Companions would

volunteer to nurse the wounded, and the Prophet, peace and blessings of Allah be upon him, would give them the choice of being in the company of her own womenfolk or that of the Mother of the Believers who had been chosen to go out with him. Rufaidah Al-Ansariyah was famous for treating the wounded at the time of the Prophet, peace and blessings of Allah be upon him. *(Asad Al-Ghayah Fi Ma'rifat Al-Sahabah)*

The Prophet, peace and blessings of Allah be upon him, set up a tent in his mosque which was like a field hospital for treating the wounded from the Battle of Al-Khandaq.

Dr. An-Naseemi explained this point as follows, "The basic principle is that it is not permissible for a man to examine or treat a non-*Mahram* woman or vice versa, because that requires looking and touching. The exception from that is cases of necessity, such as if there is no female doctor whose skills the patient trusts, or there is no female doctor working in that specialty, or because the Muslim men are needed for *Jihad*."

*****

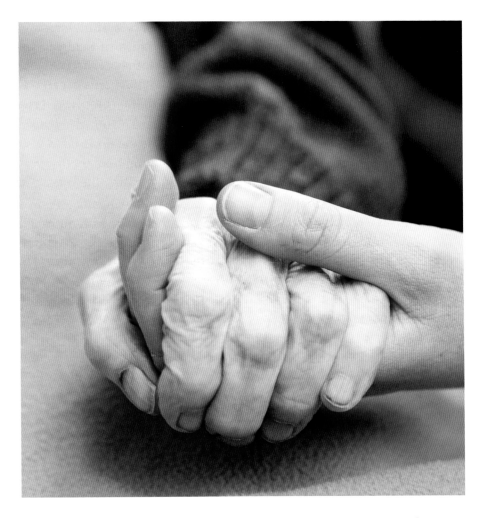

Etiquette of Visiting the Sick

This is part of the Islamic etiquette which is addressed to all Muslims; the doctor is singled out because of his direct contact with his patients.

In addition to the fact that the doctor is doing his job, he should also observe this etiquette because it is among the rights that one Muslim has over another, thus he will be doing his job in the most perfect manner.

Visiting the sick is the way of the Prophet, peace and blessings of Allah be upon him, and it is religious etiquette because the Prophet, peace and blessings of Allah be upon him, enjoined it and spoke of its virtue and reward.

Al-Bara' Ibn 'Azib, may Allah be pleased with him, said, "The Prophet, peace and blessings of Allah be upon him, enjoined us to do seven things and forbade us to do seven things. He enjoined us to visit the sick …" (Agreed upon)

It was narrated that Abu Hurairah, may Allah be pleased with him, said, "I heard the Messenger of Allah, peace and blessings of Allah be upon him, say: 'The rights of one Muslim over another are five: returning the greeting of Salam, visiting the sick, attending funerals, accepting invitations, and saying *Yarhamuk-Allah* (may Allah have mercy on you) to one who sneezes'." (Agreed upon)

It was narrated from Abu Hurairah that the Messenger of Allah, peace and blessings of Allah be upon him, said: "Allah, may He be Glorified and Exalted, will say on the Day of Resurrection: O son of Adam, I fell sick and you did not visit Me. He will say: O Lord, how could I visit You when You are the Lord of the Worlds? He will say: Did you not know that My slave so-and-so was sick but you did not visit him? Do you not know that if you had visited him you would have found Me with him? O son of Adam, I asked you for food and you did not feed Me. He will say: O Lord, how could I feed You when You are the Lord of the Worlds? He said: Did you not know that My slave so-and-so asked you for food, but you did not feed him? Do you not know that if you had fed him, you would have found that with Me? O son of Adam, I asked you for water and you did not give Me to drink. He will say: O Lord, how could I give you to drink when You are the Lord of the Worlds? He will say: My slave so-and-so asked you for water and you did not give him to drink. If you had given him to drink you would have found that with Me." (Narrated by Muslim)

It was narrated from Thawban, may Allah be pleased with him, that the Prophet, peace and blessings of Allah be upon him, said: "Whoever visits a sick person will remain in an orchard of Paradise." It was said, 'O Messenger of Allah, what is an orchard of Paradise?' He said: "Its fruits."

It is *Sunnah* for the visitor to pray for healing. Praying for him involves good words and comfort for him, and reminds him to turn to Allah, for He is the One Who can take away sickness and grant healing. In this way, the sick person will feel more reassured.

It was narrated from 'A'ishah, may Allah be pleased with her, that when the Messenger of Allah, peace and blessings of Allah be upon him, visited a sick person, he would say: "Remove the suffering, Lord of mankind, and heal me, for You are the Healer. There is no healing except Your healing, the healing which does not leave any illness behind."

The Prophet of Mercy, peace and blessings of Allah be upon him, pointed to an important aspect of visiting the sick, whether the visitor is a doctor or a relative or friend, which is that visitors should not say in the presence of the patient anything that may make him afraid or despair; rather, they should do that which will comfort him and make him happy.

> It was narrated that Umm Salamah, may Allah be pleased with her, said, "The Messenger of Allah, peace and blessings of Allah be upon him, said: "When you visit a sick or dying person, say good things, for the angels say *Ameen* to whatever you say." (Narrated by Muslim)

Islam is concerned with comforting the sick person and lifting his hopes. Ibn Al-Qayyim, may Allah have Mercy upon him, commented on the words of the Prophet, peace and blessings of Allah be upon him: "For every disease there is a remedy" by saying: This *Hadith* strengthens the morale of the patient and the doctor and encourages them to seek the remedy. If the sick person feels that there is a cure for his sickness, his hopes will be raised and his despair will be reduced.

Hence, we may understand how Islam changed visiting the sick from a quick social visit to a spiritual remedy which raises the patient's spirits and strengthens his hope of healing, in addition to showing care and support to him and his family. And Allah knows best.

References

1. 1. *Ihya' 'Uloom Ad-Deen*
2. 2. *Al-Majmoo' Jami' Al-Usool Fi Ahadeeth Al-Rasool*
3. *Al-Tibb An-Nabawi Wal-'Ilm Al-Hadith* by An-Naseemi
4. *Al-Tadawi Wal-Mas'ooliyah Al-Tibbiyah*
5. *Majmoo' Al-Fatawa*
6. *Al-Tibb An-Nabawi*
7. *Muhadarat Fi Amrad Al-Taghdhiyah Wal-Tasammumat*
8. *Akhlaq Al-Tabeeb* by Al-Razi
9. *Fat'h Al-Bari Fi Sharh Saheeh Al-Bukhari*
10. *Al-Wajeez Fil-Islam Wal-Tibb* by Al-Shatti
11. *Al-Tabeeb Adabuhu wa Fiqhuhu* by Al-Saba'i
12. *Al-Tadawi Wal-Mas'ooliyah Al-Tibbiyah Fil-Shari'ah Al-Islamiyah* by Aal Al-Sheikh
13. *Fiqh Al-Tabeeb wa Adabuhu* by Abu Ghuddah
14. *Rawai' Al-Tibb Al-Islami.*

*****

The Qur'an and
Its Effect on Healing

Allah, the Exalted, says:

﴿ وَنُنَزِّلُ مِنَ ٱلْقُرْءَانِ مَا هُوَ شِفَآءٌ وَرَحْمَةٌ لِّلْمُؤْمِنِينَ وَلَا يَزِيدُ ٱلظَّٰلِمِينَ إِلَّا خَسَارًا ﴾

"And We send down of the Qur'an that which is a healing and a mercy to those who believe (in Islamic Monotheism and act on it), and it increases the Zalimoon (polytheists and wrongdoers) nothing but loss" (Soorah Al-Isra, 17:82).

﴿ ٱللَّهُ نَزَّلَ أَحْسَنَ ٱلْحَدِيثِ كِتَٰبًا مُّتَشَٰبِهًا مَّثَانِيَ تَقْشَعِرُّ مِنْهُ جُلُودُ ٱلَّذِينَ يَخْشَوْنَ رَبَّهُمْ ثُمَّ تَلِينُ جُلُودُهُمْ وَقُلُوبُهُمْ إِلَىٰ ذِكْرِ ٱللَّهِ ذَٰلِكَ هُدَى ٱللَّهِ يَهْدِي بِهِۦ مَن يَشَآءُ وَمَن يُضْلِلِ ٱللَّهُ فَمَا لَهُۥ مِنْ هَادٍ ﴾

"Allah has sent down the Best Statement, a Book (this Qur'an), its parts resembling each other (in goodness and truth) (and) oft-repeated. The skins of those who fear their Lord shiver from it (when they recite it or hear it). Then their skin and their heart soften to the remembrance of Allah. That is the Guidance of Allah. He guides therewith whom He wills; and whomever Allah sends astray, for him there is no guide" (Soorah Al-Zumar, 39:23)

Scientific studies and researches were conducted in this field by Dr. Ahmad Al-Qadi, the head of the administration committee of the Islamic Medical Institute for Teaching and Research in America, and consultant physician at a clinic in Panama City, Florida; he carried out experiments involving the physiological and psychological effect of the Holy Qur'an on people. This experiment was done in two stages.

- First stage

The aim was to prove whether Qur'an has any effect on the functions of the body, and to measure this effect, if present. The result was that 97 percent of those who were subjected to this research, both Muslims and non-Muslims, both Arabic-speakers and those who had no knowledge of Arabic, showed functional changes which were indicative of spontaneous changes in nerve tension, as the Holy Qur'an had a calming effect on tension, which was recorded on the most advanced electronic equipment, connected to a computer, to measure physiological changes in the body.

It is well-known that tension leads to lowering of the body's immunity, which in turn leads to imbalance in internal functions. Thus, the calming effect of the Qur'an may lead to strengthening of the immune system and enabling it to resist disease or recover from it.

- Second stage

This was aimed at finding out whether the calming effect and the physiological changes to which it led was indeed the result of the Qur'anic words in and of themselves, regardless of whether they were understood by the listener or not. Thus, non-Muslim volunteers who did not know Arabic listened to a recitation of the Qur'an and readings of non-Qur'anic passages that were made to sound like Qur'anic recitation, so that the volunteers would not be able to distinguish between them, because of their ignorance of Arabic. The results were positive, as follows:

The calming effect of Qur'an on the volunteers was 56 percent, and the calming effect of non-Qur'anic recitation was similar, 53 percent. These results were presented to the seventeenth annual conference of

the Medical Association in St. Louis, Missouri.
It was done in the following manner:

- ## Equipment

Equipment for measuring and treating tension was attached to a Medec 2002 computer which was invented and developed by the Medical Center of Boston University and the Davicon Company of Boston. This equipment measured reactions that indicated tension in two ways:

a) Psychological testing via the computer

b) Watching and measuring physiological changes in the body

This integrated system included the following features:

- A computer program for administering a psychological test and watching for and measuring physiological changes and printing the results

- An Apple 2 E computer equipped with two mobile disk drives, screen and printer

- Electronic measuring device with 4 channels, two channels for measuring electrical currents in the muscles which show nerve and muscle reactions; a channel for measuring electrical impulses passing through the skin, and a channel for measuring the rate of blood circulation in the body, number of heart beats and skin temperature.

With regard to the electric current in the muscles, they increased with an increase in tension, which in turn caused increased contraction of muscles. To measure these changes, an electric receptor was used on the skin surface, placed on the forehead.

With regard to receptivity of the skin, it is affected by the presence of sweat on the skin, so it increases when more sweat is produced and decreases when less sweat is produced. Tension increases the secretion of sweat on the skin, but calmness and absence of tension leads to a reduction of moisture on the skin. Hence, its ability to transmit electricity is reduced. To measure these changes, a clip was attached to a fingertip.

The amount of blood passing through the skin and the skin

temperature are indicative of expansion or contraction of the capillaries; to measure these changes, an electrical sensor was attached to a fingertip and any change in the volume of blood flowing through the skin showed immediately on the screen, along with the heart rate. With an increase in tension, the capillaries contract and the amount of blood flowing through the capillaries of the skin decreases, and the skin temperature and heart rate both fall.

When the person is calm and there is no tension, the capillaries expand and the volume of blood flowing through the skin increases and there is a rise in temperature and a decrease in the heart rate.

• Methodology

Two hundred and ten experiments were carried out on five volunteers, three males and two females whose ages varied from 17 to 40 years, with an average age of 22 years.

All of the volunteers were non-Muslims who had no knowledge of Arabic. These experiments were carried out in 42 sessions, with 5 experiments in each session, so that the total number of experiments was 210. First, Qur'anic Verses in Arabic were recited to the volunteers in 85 sessions, and in a further 85 sessions, non-Qur'anic matter in Arabic was recited to the volunteers, in which attention was paid to making the non-Qur'anic readings appear identical to Qur'anic Verses in terms of sound, pronunciation and the way it falls on the ear. The volunteers did not listen to any recitation in 40 other sessions, but during these silent sessions the volunteers sat comfortably with their eyes closed, as they did in the 170 other experiments, during which they listened to Qur'anic and non-Qur'anic Arabic recitation.

The non-Qur'anic Arabic recitations were used as an equivalent to the non-medicinal placebo and were made similar to Qur'anic recitation so that the volunteers would not be able to distinguish between Qur'an and non-Qur'anic readings. The aim of that was to find out if the Qur'anic wording had any physiological effect on the one who could not understand its meaning, and whether this effect was really the effect of the Qur'anic wording and not the effect of the sound of Arabic being recited when it was foreign to the ears of the listener.

The experiments in which the volunteers did not listen to anything were aimed at finding out whether the physiological effects were the result of sitting in a comfortable environment with the eyes closed.

It became apparent from the first experiments that sitting quietly without listening to any recitation did not have any calming effect on tension. Therefore, later experiments were limited to comparing Qur'anic and non-Qur'anic readings.

Attention was paid to continually changing the order of Qur'anic recitations and other readings; sometimes the Qur'anic recitation came before the other reading, and sometimes it came after the other reading, and so on.

The volunteers were aware that one reading was Qur'an and the other was not, but they were not able to recognize the type of reading being used in any particular experiment.

The ways of monitoring the experiments in this study were limited to using channels for measuring electric current in the muscles, which was part of the Medec equipment described above, using an electric sensor on the skin surface, placed on the forehead.

The measurements which were compared and recorded in this study included the average voltage in the muscles, in addition to the level of oscillation in the electric current at any time during the experiment; the extent of the muscle's sensitivity to light; and the percentage of voltage at the end of each experiment compared to the beginning. Each of these measurements was recorded electronically on the computer.

The reason why this method of observation was preferred was that it produces real, accurate figures which are useful for comparing and evaluating results. In any experiment or group of experiments, the result that led to a reduction of voltage in the muscles was regarded as positive, because this was taken as a better indicator of effectiveness than the calming or reduction of tension in comparison to the other remedies used on the same volunteer in the same session.

- ## Results

The results were positive in 65 percent of the experiments in which Qur'anic recitations were used. This means that the voltage of the muscles was lower in these experiments, which indicates that it had the effect of calming tension, whereas this effect appeared in only 33 percent of the experiments involving non-Qur'anic readings.

With a number of volunteers it was possible to get the same positive results as with the Qur'anic readings, despite the fact that the order of recitation was changed which made these results more certain.

- ## Discussion of the results and conclusion of the study

The initial results of our Qur'anic study show that the Qur'an has a positive effect in calming tension and it was possible to record these effects both qualitatively and quantitatively. The effect appeared in the form of changes in the electric current in the muscles and changes in the skin's ability to conduct electricity and changes in the blood circulation, which were accompanied by changes in the heart rate and the volume of blood in the skin and the temperature of the skin.

All of these changes indicate a change in the function of the autonomic nervous system which in turn affects other faculties and functions in the body. Therefore there are unlimited possibilities for the physiological impact that the Qur'an may have.

It is commonly known that tension leads to reduction of immune strength which may be because of the secretion of cortisol or other reactions between the nervous system and the endocrine system. Hence, it is logical to assume that the calming effect on tension could lead to improvement of the immune function in the body, which in turn will improve the body's ability to fight disease or recover from it. This applies to contagious diseases, cancerous tumors and so on.

The results of a comparative study indicate that the words of the Qur'an themselves, regardless of whether their meanings are understood or not, have a calming physiological effect on tension in the human body.

It is worth mentioning in this context that the results mentioned are initial results of a number of limited experiments with a small number of volunteers.

The Qur'anic research program is still going on and is aimed at achieving a number of goals, such as the following:

- Carrying out a greater number of experiments on a larger number of volunteers to confirm the current results

- Comparing the effect of different verses of Qur'an with the effect of the Qur'anic meanings whether in Arabic or in translation

- Comparing the effect of different verses such as verses which speak of glad tidings and verses which speak of punishment

- Comparing the effect of Qur'an with the effect of other modalities that are used to calm tension

- Testing the long-term healing effects of Qur'an on the body's immune function, whether it has to do with the cells or the antibodies in the blood

- Testing the medicinal effect of the Qur'an in special situations, especially in physical cases, and trying to analyze this effect in precise, scientific ways

It is clear from what is mentioned above that this program of Qur'anic research is a lengthy and complex program that requires a number of independent studies and will take a number of years to complete.

But it is a very important subject and the results are promising; we hope that it will be of scientific benefit.

Allah, the Exalted, says in His Holy Book:

﴿ اللَّهُ نَزَّلَ أَحْسَنَ الْحَدِيثِ كِتَابًا مُتَشَابِهًا مَثَانِيَ تَقْشَعِرُّ مِنْهُ جُلُودُ الَّذِينَ يَخْشَوْنَ رَبَّهُمْ ثُمَّ تَلِينُ جُلُودُهُمْ وَقُلُوبُهُمْ إِلَى ذِكْرِ اللَّهِ ذَلِكَ هُدَى اللَّهِ يَهْدِي بِهِ مَن يَشَاءُ وَمَن يُضْلِلِ اللَّهُ فَمَا لَهُ مِنْ هَادٍ ﴾

"Allah has sent down the Best Statement, a Book (this Qur'an), its parts resembling each other (in goodness and truth) (and) oft-repeated. The skins of those who fear their Lord shiver from it (when they recite it or hear it). Then their skin and their hearts soften to the remembrance of Allah. That is the Guidance of Allah. He guides therewith whom He wills; and whomever Allah sends astray, for him there is no guide." (Soorah Al-Zumar, 39:23)

﴿ إِنَّمَا الْمُؤْمِنُونَ الَّذِينَ إِذَا ذُكِرَ اللَّهُ وَجِلَتْ قُلُوبُهُمْ وَإِذَا تُلِيَتْ عَلَيْهِمْ ءَايَاتُهُ زَادَتْهُمْ إِيمَانًا وَعَلَى رَبِّهِمْ يَتَوَكَّلُونَ ﴾

"The Believers are only those who, when Allah is mentioned, feel a fear in their hearts and when His Verses (of this Qur'an) are recited unto them, they (i.e. the Verses) increase their Faith; and they put their trust in their Lord (Alone)." (Soorah Al-Anfal, 8:2)

* * * * *

Chapter: 6

Wheat Field on a Summer Day

Effects of Qur'an on Correcting Plant Growth

An Arab researcher and university professor, who is known for his work both in the Arab world and internationally, conducted the following experiment which we will discuss here, which is proved by Science and confirmed by the words of Allah, the Exalted:

﴾ تُسَبِّحُ لَهُ السَّمَوَاتُ السَّبْعُ وَالْأَرْضُ وَمَن فِيهِنَّ وَإِن مِّن شَيْءٍ إِلَّا يُسَبِّحُ بِحَمْدِهِ وَلَكِن لَّا تَفْقَهُونَ تَسْبِيحَهُمْ إِنَّهُ كَانَ حَلِيمًا غَفُورًا ﴿

"The seven heavens and the Earth and all that is therein, glorify Him and there is not a thing but glorifies His Praise. But you understand not their glorification. Truly, He is Ever-Forbearing, Oft-Forgiving."
(Soorah Al-Isra, 17:44)

﴾ أَلَمْ تَرَ أَنَّ اللَّهَ يُسَبِّحُ لَهُ مَن فِي السَّمَوَاتِ وَالْأَرْضِ وَالطَّيْرُ صَافَّاتٍ كُلٌّ قَدْ عَلِمَ صَلَاتَهُ وَتَسْبِيحَهُ وَاللَّهُ عَلِيمٌ بِمَا يَفْعَلُونَ ﴿

"See you not (O Muhammad ﷺ) that Allah, He it is Whom glorify whosoever is in the heavens and the Earth, and the birds with wings outspread (in their flight)? Of each one He (Allah) knows indeed his Salat (prayer) and his glorification [or everyone knows his Salat (prayer) and his glorification]; and Allah is All-Aware of what they do." (Soorah Al-Noor, 24:41)

﴿ هُوَ ٱللَّهُ ٱلْخَالِقُ ٱلْبَارِئُ ٱلْمُصَوِّرُ لَهُ ٱلْأَسْمَاءُ ٱلْحُسْنَىٰ يُسَبِّحُ لَهُ مَا فِي ٱلسَّمَٰوَٰتِ وَٱلْأَرْضِ وَهُوَ ٱلْعَزِيزُ ٱلْحَكِيمُ ﴾

"He is Allah, the Creator, the Inventor of all things, the Bestower of forms. To Him belong the Best Names. All that is in the heavens and the Earth glorify Him. And He is the Almighty, the All-Wise7." (Soorah Al-Hashr, 59:24)

The word *Ma'* (translated here as "all that…") in this Verse refers to irrational creatures.

﴿ وَٱلنَّجْمُ وَٱلشَّجَرُ يَسْجُدَانِ ﴾

"And the herbs (or stars) and the trees both prostrate themselves (before Allah)." (Soorah Ar-Rahman, 55:6)

This researcher says, "Plants, like heavenly bodies and other creations of Allah, have feelings and can hear, and they respond positively or negatively to the external influences around them. This is the conclusion of my research."

This researcher conducted an experiment in the garden of the science faculty in 1997. He set up four plastic tents of the same size, and planted wheat of a certain type inside them. These tents were of the same size, with equal amounts of soil, and he planted the wheat in them to the same depth, and fertilized them with equal amounts of a certain fertilizer, and watered them equally, then he chose one of his students to recite the following *Soorahs* of the Qur'an: *Ya Seen, Al-Fati'hah, Al-Ikhlas,* and *Aayat Al-Kursi,* twice a week to the plants in the first tent; in the second tent, a student was to bring plants and tear them apart and mistreat them in front of the plants, and speak harshly to them, also twice a week; in the third tent a student was to strike the plants with a branding iron and cut their small leaves – so there were plants in front of which other plants were mistreated and plants which were themselves mistreated – and plants before which Verses of the Book of Allah were recited. The plants in the fourth tent were left to grow naturally, and this was called the "control" tent. What was the result?

The result that was presented in a scientific conference was that the plants, to which the Qur'an was recited, grew 44 percent taller than the control plants in the fourth tent and yielded a crop 140 percent bigger than that yielded in the control tent. The plants in the second and third tents, which were either mistreated or saw other plants being mistreated, grew 35 percent shorter and their yield fell to 80 percent. This is a scientific explanation and proof of *Barakah* (blessing). When the believer sows seeds while reciting Qur'an and cheerfully, remembering Allah, Most High, all the time, this *Dhikr* (remembrance) in front of the plants increases the yield.

Thirty years ago, as far as I remember, I saw with my own eyes a grain of wheat in Ghootat Dimashq (an agricultural area near Damascus) that produced thirty-five stems. I took one of these stems and opened it, and it contained fifty grains. I worked it out, 50 times 35, and realized that there were 1,750 grains from one single grain.

This scientist says, One *dunam* now gives 1,500 kilograms, but it is possible to get 14 tons according to the Verse:

﴿ مَّثَلُ ٱلَّذِينَ يُنفِقُونَ أَمْوَٰلَهُمْ فِى سَبِيلِ ٱللَّهِ كَمَثَلِ حَبَّةٍ أَنۢبَتَتْ سَبْعَ سَنَابِلَ فِى كُلِّ سُنۢبُلَةٍ مِّا۟ئَةُ حَبَّةٍ وَٱللَّهُ يُضَٰعِفُ لِمَن يَشَآءُ وَٱللَّهُ وَٰسِعٌ عَلِيمٌ ﴾

"The likeness of those who spend their wealth in the way of Allah, is as the likeness of a grain (of corn); it grows seven ears, and each ear has a hundred grains. Allah gives manifold increase to whom He wills. And Allah is All-Sufficient for His creatures' needs, All-Knower." (Soorah Al-Baqarah, 2:261).

Scarcity of food is a reminder and admonishment from Allah. The one who says that there is a shortage of food in the world and that there will be wars for wheat and for water is, in my opinion, uttering nonsense.

A reputed scientific magazine has reported that a cloud has been discovered in space which could fill the oceans of Earth sixty times daily with freshwater. Thus, there may never be a need to launch "wars for water".

Allah says:

﴿ وَأَلَّوِ ٱسْتَقَـٰمُوا۟ عَلَى ٱلطَّرِيقَةِ لَأَسْقَيْنَـٰهُم مَّآءً غَدَقًا ﴾

"If they (non-Muslims) had believed in Allah, and went on the Right Way (i.e. Islam) We would surely have bestowed on them water (rain) in abundance." (Soorah Al-Jinn, 72:16)

﴿ وَلَوْ أَنَّ أَهْلَ ٱلْقُرَىٰٓ ءَامَنُوا۟ وَٱتَّقَوْا۟ لَفَتَحْنَا عَلَيْهِم بَرَكَـٰتٍ
مِّنَ ٱلسَّمَآءِ وَٱلْأَرْضِ وَلَـٰكِن كَذَّبُوا۟ فَأَخَذْنَـٰهُم بِمَا كَانُوا۟ يَكْسِبُونَ ﴾

"And if the people of the towns had believed and had the Taqwa (piety), certainly, We should have opened for them blessings from the heaven and the Earth, but they belied (the Messengers). So We took them (with punishment) for what they used to earn (polytheism and crimes)." (Soorah Al-A'raf, 7:96)

﴿ وَلَوْ أَنَّهُمْ أَقَامُوا۟ ٱلتَّوْرَىٰةَ وَٱلْإِنجِيلَ وَمَآ أُنزِلَ إِلَيْهِم مِّن رَّبِّهِمْ لَأَكَلُوا۟ مِن
فَوْقِهِمْ وَمِن تَحْتِ أَرْجُلِهِمۚ مِّنْهُمْ أُمَّةٌ مُّقْتَصِدَةٌۖ وَكَثِيرٌ مِّنْهُمْ سَآءَ مَا يَعْمَلُونَ ﴾

"And if only they had acted according to the Tawrat, the Injeel, and what has (now) been sent down to them from their Lord (the Qur'an), they would surely, have gotten provision from above them and from underneath their feet. There are from among them people who are

on the right course (i.e. they act on the Revelation and believe in Prophet Muhammad ﷺ), but many of them do evil deeds." (Soorah Al-Ma'idah, 5:66)

You may be amazed that these plants listen to the Qur'an and respond to it, but why are you surprised? Allah, the Exalted, says:

﴿ لَوۡ أَنزَلۡنَا هَٰذَا ٱلۡقُرۡءَانَ عَلَىٰ جَبَلٍ لَّرَأَيۡتَهُۥ خَٰشِعٗا مُّتَصَدِّعٗا مِّنۡ خَشۡيَةِ ٱللَّهِۚ وَتِلۡكَ ٱلۡأَمۡثَٰلُ نَضۡرِبُهَا لِلنَّاسِ لَعَلَّهُمۡ يَتَفَكَّرُونَ ﴾

"Had We sent down this Qur'an on a mountain, you would surely have seen it humbling itself and rent asunder by the fear of Allah The Exalted. Such are the parables which We put forward to mankind that they may reflect." (Al-Hashr, 59:21)

Which is more alive – a plant or a mountain?

The Qur'an was revealed to Prophet Muhammad, peace and blessings of Allah be upon him, to be a guidance. Man for whose sake it was revealed neglects it, while plants respond to it. Allah, Most High, says:

﴿ تُسَبِّحُ لَهُ ٱلسَّمَٰوَٰتُ ٱلسَّبۡعُ وَٱلۡأَرۡضُ وَمَن فِيهِنَّۚ وَإِن مِّن شَيۡءٍ إِلَّا يُسَبِّحُ بِحَمۡدِهِۦ وَلَٰكِن لَّا تَفۡقَهُونَ تَسۡبِيحَهُمۡۚ إِنَّهُۥ كَانَ حَلِيمًا غَفُورًا ﴾

"The seven heavens and the Earth and all that is therein, glorify Him and there is not a thing but glorifies His Praise. But you understand not their glorification. Truly, He is Ever-Forbearing, Oft-Forgiving." (Soorah Al-Isra, 17:44)

﴿ لَوۡ أَنزَلۡنَا هَٰذَا ٱلۡقُرۡءَانَ عَلَىٰ جَبَلٍ لَّرَأَيۡتَهُۥ خَٰشِعٗا مُّتَصَدِّعٗا مِّنۡ خَشۡيَةِ ٱللَّهِۚ وَتِلۡكَ ٱلۡأَمۡثَٰلُ نَضۡرِبُهَا لِلنَّاسِ لَعَلَّهُمۡ يَتَفَكَّرُونَ ﴾

"Had We sent down this Qur'an on a mountain," – not to a living plant – "you would surely have seen it humbling itself and rent asunder by the fear of Allah. Such are the parables which We put forward to mankind that they may reflect." (Soorah Al-Hashr, 59:21)

﴿ وَٱلنَّجۡمُ وَٱلشَّجَرُ يَسۡجُدَانِ ۝ فَبِأَيِّ ءَالَآءِ رَبِّكُمَا تُكَذِّبَانِ ﴾

"And the herbs (or stars) and the trees both prostrate themselves (before Allah) Then which of the Blessings of your Lord will you both (Jinn and men) deny?" (Soorah Ar-Rahman, 55:6,13)

If this is the attitude of plants toward the Holy Qur'an, then is it possible that man, who is an honored creature, and to whom the Qur'an is primarily addressed, can ignore this Qur'an which guides to the best to such an extent that these words are applicable to the Muslims:

﴿ وَقَالَ ٱلرَّسُولُ يَٰرَبِّ إِنَّ قَوْمِى ٱتَّخَذُواْ هَٰذَا ٱلْقُرْءَانَ مَهْجُورًا ﴾

"And the Messenger (Muhammad ﷺ) will say: 'O my Lord! Verily, my people deserted this Qur'an (neither listened to it nor acted on its laws and teachings).'" (Soorah Al-Furqan, 25:30)

(*Al-'Ijaz Al-'Ilmi* by Dr. An-Nabulsi)

*****

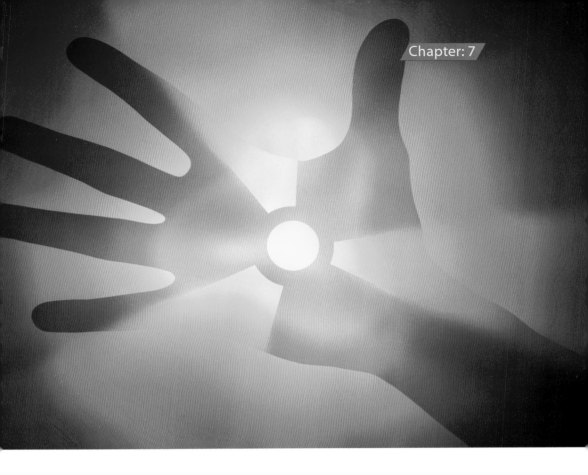

Chapter: 7

Quarantine

Quarantine is regarded as one of the most important means of stopping the spread of epidemics in modern times. It prevents anyone from entering the regions in which the epidemic is widespread and mixing with the people there, and prevents the people of those regions from coming out, whether a person is infected with the epidemic or not.

In numerous narrations, the Prophet, peace and blessings of Allah be upon him, has clearly described the principles of quarantine. He forbade people to enter lands affected by the plague, and he also forbade the inhabitants of that land to come out of it. Moreover, he regarded that as equivalent to fleeing from the battlefield, which is a

major sin, and he described the one who bore it with patience as being equal in reward to the martyr.

Al-Bukhari and Muslim narrated in their *Saheehain* from 'Abdullah Ibn 'Abbas, may Allah be pleased with him, that 'Umar Ibn Al-Khattab, may Allah be pleased with him, set out for Syria, and when he was in Sargh he was met by the commander of the troops, Abu 'Ubaidah Ibn Al-Jarrah, may Allah be pleased with him, and his companions, who told him that pestilence had broken out in Syria.

Ibn 'Abbas said: " 'Umar said, 'Call the first *Muhajireen* (emigrants) for me.' So I called them, and he consulted them and told them that pestilence had broken out in Syria. They had a difference of opinion. Some of them said, 'You have come out for a purpose and we do not think that you should go back.' Some said, 'You have the remainder of the people and the Companions of the Messenger of Allah, peace and blessings of Allah be upon him, with you; we do not think that you should continue with them to where this pestilence is.' He said, 'You may go.'

Then he said, 'Call the *Ansar* for me,' so I called them for him, and he consulted them, and they did the same as the *Muhajireen* did, and had the same difference of opinion. He said, 'You may go.' Then he said, 'Call for me those who are here from the elders of Quraish who migrated after the Conquest of Makkah.' I called them and no two men among them differed. They said, 'We think that you should go back with the people and not take them to where this pestilence is prevalent.'

At this, 'Umar, may Allah be pleased with him, called out to the people, 'In the morning I will be mounted, so get on your mounts in the morning.' Abu 'Ubaidah said, 'Are you fleeing from the decree of Allah?' 'Umar said, 'Would that someone other than you had said that, O Abu 'Ubaidah! (because 'Umar did not like to disagree with

him) 'Yes, we are fleeing from the decree of Allah to the decree of Allah. Do you think that if you had camels and they came down into a valley that had two sides, one that was green and verdant and one that was barren, and you took them to graze in the verdant side, would that not be by the decree of Allah? And if you took them to graze on the barren side, would that not also be by the decree of Allah?'

Then 'Abdur Rahman Ibn 'Awf, may Allah be pleased with him, came, who had been absent on some errand, and said, 'I have some knowledge about that. I heard the Messenger of Allah, peace and blessings of Allah be upon him, say: If you hear that it (the plague) is in a land, do not go there, and if it breaks out in a land where you are, do not leave, fleeing from it'."

On hearing this, 'Umar, may Allah be pleased with him, praised

Allah, the Exalted, then he went back.

Imam Ahmad, may Allah have Mercy upon him, narrated that 'A'ishah, may Allah be pleased with her, said: "The Messenger of Allah, peace and blessings of Allah be upon him, said 'My *Ummah* (nation) will not be destroyed except by means of stabbing and the plague.' I said, 'O Messenger of Allah, this stabbing we know about, but what is this plague?' He said: 'A gland like the gland of a sick camel; the one who stays (in the land where it is) is like a martyr, and the one who flees from it is like the one who flees from the battlefield'."

The Prophetic miracle here can be seen in the fact that these narrations forbid the person who is living in the land where the epidemic is from leaving it even if he is not affected. The reason for forbidding people to enter that land may be obvious and understandable, but the reason for forbidding the person who lives in the affected land from leaving it, even if he is sound and healthy, is not obvious, rather logic and reason would dictate that the healthy person who lives in a land affected by an epidemic should flee to another land that is safe so that he will not be affected by the disease. But the reason was not known until later period when science and knowledge advanced further.

Modern medicine – as Dr. Muhammad 'Ali Al-Bar stated – has proved that the healthy person in an epidemic area may be a carrier of the germs that cause the epidemic. Many epidemics infect many people, but not everyone whose body is infected by the germs gets sick. How many people carry the germs without showing any symptoms? Meningitis, typhoid, dysentery, tuberculosis, and even cholera and the plague may affect many people without any initial sign of sickness; the individual may appear very healthy but he is transmitting the disease to other healthy people.

There is an incubation period which is the time that precedes the appearance of symptoms from the time when the germs first enter the body and begin to multiply, until they reach their peak. During this period it is not obvious to the individual that he is suffering from any sickness, but after a period which may be long or short – depending on the type of sickness and the germ that he is carrying – the symptoms of the hidden disease appear in the body.

The incubation period of influenza, for example, is one or two days, while the incubation period of viral liver infection (hepatitis) may be as long as six months. The bacteria that cause tuberculosis may remain dormant in the body for a number of years without showing any symptoms, but soon after that period, it will start to spread throughout the body.

How could Muhammad, peace and blessings of Allah be upon him, have known all of this? What taught him the facts when he was an unlettered man who could neither read nor write? It is Divine knowledge and Divine inspiration which preceded all of this modern science and knowledge, so that this religion would remain as a witness over humanity in every time and at place, and so that those who were to be destroyed (for their rejecting the Faith) might be destroyed after a clear evidence, and those who were to live (i.e. Believers) might live after a clear evidence (cf. *Soorah Al-Anfal* 8:42).

✻✻✻✻✻

The Plague

The plague is an infectious, epidemic disease caused by rod-shaped bacteria that were discovered by the scientist, Yersin in 1849, and thus, it is called after him – *Yersinas pestis*. The plague appears like waves, sweeping over lands and peoples, harvesting thousands of souls on its way. It usually affects rats and is transmitted to man via fleas. It affects the lymph nodes in the armpits, back of the knees and crease of the belly, causing swellings which increase in size and split, becoming like boils. It may also affect the lungs and throat with or without becoming very severe. An epidemic of this nature struck Syria in 18 A.H., which was called the plague of Amwas (Emmaus), after a small town of that name between Jerusalem and Ramallah where it first appeared, then it spread throughout Syria.

Al-Waqidi said, "In the plague of Amwas, twenty-five thousand Muslims of Syria died." Others said the number was thirty thousand, as was stated by Ibn Katheer in *Al-Bidayah Wan-Nihayah*.

According to the *Hadith* narrated by Ahmad on the authority of 'A'ishah, may Allah be pleased with her, the Prophet, peace and blessings of Allah be upon him, said: "My Ummah will not be destroyed except by means of stabbing and the plague." I said, "O Messenger of Allah, this stabbing we know about, but what is this plague? He said:"A gland like the gland of a sick camel; the one who stays (in the land where it is) is like a martyr, and the one who flees from it is like one who flees from the battlefield."

Fleas in Hair/Animal Hair

This narration is the basis for quarantine, which was not known until the twentieth century. If a contagious epidemic appears in some land, then quarantine is to be imposed on it. So no one should enter it lest he will be exposing himself to doom and be infected by the epidemic, and no one who is in that land is allowed to leave, lest he be infected with the disease which is still in its incubation period, and this carries the disease outside of that land and spreads it further. Hence, no one is allowed to leave until he has been vaccinated against the germs that cause this disease and has been placed in quarantine where he spends the incubation period of the disease in isolation. Each epidemic has its own, different incubation period. If the individual does not show any sign of the disease in that period then he is safe.

Sick Camels Should not be Brought to Where Healthy Ones are

It was narrated from Abu Salamah that he heard Abu Hurairah say, the Prophet, peace and blessings of Allah be upon him, said: "A sick camel should not be brought to where a healthy one is." (Al-Bukhari and Muslim)

Ibn Hajar, may Allah have Mercy on him, said: This is a prohibition. The owner of the sick camel is forbidden to bring it to where the healthy camel is. This is in accordance with the narration quoted above which says that contagion occurs by the Decree of Allah, the Almighty, and it may happen to animals too, just as it happens to humans.

It is worth mentioning that there is no contradiction with the narration in which the Prophet, peace and blessings of Allah be upon him, said: "There is no *'Adwa* (contagion, transmission of infectious disease without the permission of Allah), no Safar (the month of Safar was regarded as "unlucky" during the *Jahiliyah*) and no *Hammah* (refers to a pre-Islamic Arab tradition described variously as a worm which infests the grave of a murder victim until he is avenged; an owl; or the bones of a dead person turned into a bird that could fly)."

A Bedouin said, "O Messenger of Allah, the camels may be healthy like deer, then a mangy camel comes and mixes with them and they all get the mange." The Prophet, peace and blessings of Allah be upon him, said: "And who infected the first one?" (Agreed upon)

The answer of the Prophet, peace and blessings of Allah be upon him, was very eloquent and astute. What it means is: From where did the mange come which infected the first one, as they claim? If he says, from another camel, then the chain will continue; if there is some other reason, let him tell us. If he says that the one who did it to the first one is the one who did it to the second, then the point is proved, which is that the one who does it to all of them is the Creator Who is Able to do all things, namely Allah, may He be Glorified and Exalted.

The narrations of the Prophet, peace and blessings of Allah be upon him, that we have quoted above, say there is no *'Adwa* (contagion), yet at the same time the Prophet, peace and blessings of Allah be upon him, said: "Flee from the leper as you would flee from a lion." (Narrated by Al-Bukhari in a *Mu'allaq* report, and by Ahmad)

And he says in the discussion here: "A sick camel should not be brought to where a healthy one is."

These narrations guide people to perfect *Tawheed* (Islamic Monotheism), and make them turn to their Creator Who created all causes and effects.

A specialist doctor said, "From what we have explained above on the topic of contagious diseases, we can clearly see the miraculous nature of the narrations of the Prophet, peace and blessings of Allah be upon him. The Prophet's narrations explain clearly that the entry of germs into the human body is not sufficient in and of itself to cause sickness; there are other factors that are not apparent to us that are ultimately responsible for the occurrence of disease."

Since the Turks found out about vaccinating cows against smallpox and about vaccinating their children, the English doctor, Edward Jenner, learned from their example, and thus the benefits of inoculation and vaccination against germs became clear. The idea of inoculation and vaccination may be summed up as introducing dead or weak germs into the healthy body, where the immune system recognizes them and makes antibodies against them so that if the real germ enters the body, its defense system is completely prepared to resist it.

Thus it is clear that the germ alone is not the cause of sickness. Hence, there is no contagion; rather, contagion occurs as the result of the Divine decree. However, we cannot deny the causes; we take precautions in the world of causes, while believing completely that they cannot bring benefit or ward off harm in and of themselves. Everything is in the hands of the Creator of causes. Thus it is clear that the narrations of the Prophet, peace and blessings of Allah be upon him, carry within them a scientific miracle that was not discovered until the twentieth century, when human knowledge of the causes of sickness and the immune system developed.

(See: *Hal Hunaka Tibb An-Nabawi?*)

Diet is the Primary Treatment

It was narrated from 'A'ishah, may Allah be pleased with her, that if a member of her family died, the women would gather together, then they would depart, except her own relatives and close friends. She would order that a pot of *Talbeenah* (barley porridge) be cooked, then some *Thareed* (a dish of meat and bread) would be made and the *Talbeenah* would be poured over it. Then she would say, "Eat some of it, for I heard the Messenger of Allah, peace and blessings of Allah be upon him, say: 'Talbeenah soothes the heart of the sick person, and it takes away some of the grief'." (Narrated by Al-Bukhari and Muslim)

What is meant by "soothes the heart of the sick person" is that it calms him, takes away worry and gives him energy.

According to a report narrated by Al-Bukhari, 'A'ishah, may Allah

Talbeenah

be pleased with her, used to order that *Talbeenah* be made, and she would say, "It is the disliked thing that is beneficial."

And it was narrated that 'A'ishah said, "If his family fell sick, the Messenger of Allah, peace and blessings of Allah be upon him, would order that soup be made. He used to say: "It strengthens the heart of the grieving one and takes away pain from the heart of the sick one just as one of you removes dirt from her face with water." (Narrated by At-Tirmidhi who said it is *saheeh Hadith*)

It was narrated that Umm Al-Mundhir Bint Qais Al-Ansariyah, may Allah be pleased with her, said, "The Messenger of Allah, peace and blessings of Allah be upon him, entered upon us, and with him was 'Ali Ibn Abi Talib, may Allah be pleased with him, who had recently recovered from an illness. We had bunches of unripe dates hanging up, and the Prophet, peace and blessings of Allah be upon him, was eating from them. 'Ali reached out to eat some, and the Prophet, peace and blessings of Allah be upon him, said to 'Ali: 'Stop, O 'Ali! You have just recovered from an illness.' I made some greens and barley for the Prophet, peace and blessings of Allah be upon him, and the Prophet, peace and blessings o f

Allah be upon him, said to 'Ali, may Allah be pleased with him: 'O 'Ali, eat some of this, for it is better for you'." (Narrated by Abu Dawood and Ibn Majah; It is a *hasan Hadith*)

With regard to the well-known saying, "Diet is the primary treatment and the stomach is the home of disease", this is not a Prophetic narration; it is most likely to be a saying of the Arab doctor, Al-Harith Ibn Kaladah, who used to say, "The head of medicine is diet."

Ibn Hajar said that Al-Asma'i said, "*Talbeenah* is a broth made from flour and bran, to which honey is added, or it was said, milk. It is called *Talbeenah* because it resembles milk (*Laban*) in its whiteness and consistency."

Abu Na'eem said in *Al-Tibb*, that it was made of flour only. Al-Baghdadi said, "*Talbeenah* is broth which may be the same consistency as milk. It is flour that is cooked, not raw. If you want to know the benefits of *Talbeenah*, then find out the benefits of barley water, especially if the bran is ground, for it is absorbed quickly and makes you feel better. It is very light food, and if it is drunk hot, it is more quickly absorbed and is more effective."

Ibn Al-Qayyim said, "Diet means two things: avoidance of that which causes sickness and avoiding that which increases it. The former is the diet of healthy people and the latter is the diet of sick people."

The basic principle concerning that is the Verse in which Allah, the Exalted, says:

$$﴿ وَإِن كُنتُم مَّرْضَىٰٓ أَوْ عَلَىٰ سَفَرٍ أَوْ جَآءَ أَحَدٌ مِّنكُم مِّنَ ٱلْغَآئِطِ أَوْ لَٰمَسْتُمُ ٱلنِّسَآءَ فَلَمْ تَجِدُواْ مَآءً فَتَيَمَّمُواْ صَعِيدًا طَيِّبًا ﴾$$

"And if you are ill, or on a journey, or one of you comes after answering the call of nature, or you have been in contact with women (by sexual relations) and you find no water, perform Tayammum with clean earth." (Soorah Al-Nisa', 4:43)

So the sick person refrains from using water because it may harm him. The most beneficial use of diet is when a person is recovering from sickness, because he has not yet regained his strength and his digestion is still weak and susceptible, so eating everything may cause

a relapse.

It should be noted that the Prophet's advice to 'Ali, may Allah be pleased with him, not to eat unripe dates was the best advice, because the unripe dates were hanging up in the house, and fruit is harmful to the one who is recovering from sickness, because it is quickly digested and the convalescent is too weak to cope with it. From a medical point of view it is heavy on the stomach, so the stomach uses up energy to digest it, which diverts that energy from the process of dealing with the remaining sickness.

When the barley and beets were placed before him, he told him to eat that, because it is among the most beneficial of food for the one who is recovering from sickness. Barley water has a cooling and nutritious effect; it is light and easy to digest, which is better for the one who is convalescing, especially if it is cooked with the beet roots. This is the best nourishment for the one whose stomach is still weak.

Talbinah soup

It should be noted that in many cases, when sick and convalescing people are told not to eat certain food but have an overwhelming desire to eat it, eating a little of it that is not too much for the system to digest will not harm them. Rather it may even be beneficial because the stomach will accept it.

Hence, the Prophet, peace and blessings of Allah be upon him, allowed Suhaib, may Allah be pleased with him, to eat a few dates, as Suhaib narrated, "The Prophet, peace and blessings of Allah be upon him, came to me and I had bread and dates before me. Prophet Muhammad said: "Come and eat." I started to eat the dates and the Prophet, peace and blessings of Allah be upon him, said: "Are you eating dates when your eye is sore?" I said, "I am chewing from the other side", and the Messenger of Allah, peace and blessings of Allah be upon him, smiled." (Narrated by Ibn Majah)

It is a true miracle that the teachings of the Prophet, peace and blessings of Allah be upon him, about diet are in complete harmony with the conclusions of modern medicine, which define diet as specific nutritional advice for the sick person, giving him a program to follow that he should not transgress, or telling him not to consume certain kinds of food and drink which are clearly harmful or may make him sick.

Diet is regarded as part of the treatment in many cases, and each sickness has its own diet or regime. The Messenger of Allah, peace and blessings of Allah be upon him, pointed to the importance of diet even during the convalescent phase. It was his teaching for the sick person to eat lighter food than usual.

He prescribed *Talbeenah* and broth because they are light foods that are easy to digest. Both of them soothe the stomach and increase its ability to digest, and they reduce the effects of grief, because heavy food when one is upset may be too difficult for the sick person to digest.

Barley was the staple food of the people of the Hejaz, because wheat was rarely available to them. Hence, *Talbeenah* was made of barley flour. Modern medical sources confirm the prescription of barley broth in diets and regimes as a light food that is easily digested. Crushed barley that has had the husk removed and has been cooked in water or milk is given to the mentally ill and to children, and is prescribed for those who are sick, have fevers, have low appetites or poor digestion.

Another example of the Prophet's teaching with regard to diet is that the patient should not be forced to eat or drink if he does not feel like eating or drinking. It was narrated that 'Uqbah Ibn 'Amir Al-Juhani, may Allah be pleased with him, said, "The Messenger of Allah, peace and blessings of Allah be upon him, said: "Do not force your sick ones to eat or drink, for Allah will give them to eat and drink." (Narrated by Ibn Majah and At-Tirmidhi, who said that it is a *ghareeb hasan Hadith*. I say: Its *Isnad* includes Bukair Ibn Yoonus Ibn Bukair, who is *Wahi Al-*

Hadith)

Ibn Al-Qayyim said, "How great is the benefit of these Prophetic words which contain Divine wisdom! That is because when the sick person has no appetite for food and drink, it is because his body is busy fighting the sickness."

Dr. 'Adil Al-Azhari said in his commentary on *Hamish Kitab Al-Tibb An-Nabawi li Ibn Al-Qayyim*, "Most sicknesses are accompanied by lack of appetite, and feeding the patient deliberately in such cases will cause him harm, because his digestive system is unable to work as it should be, which will lead to indigestion and a worsening of his illness. Every patient has specific food that he should eat, which should be easy to digest and in small quantities. One of the signs of recovery is when the patient regains his appetite."

Dr. An-Naseemi confirms, "The wisdom of Allah decrees that there are stores of energy in the body which are utilized at times of deprivation, so the patient's caretakers should not be overly concerned about his lack of appetite during his sickness. The stomach may not be able to cope with extra food or to cope with food at all, and that may lead to nausea and vomiting. Hence, it is not permissible to force the patient to eat when he does not want to."

References:

1. *Jami' Al-Usool Fi Ahadeeth Ar-Rasool*

2. *Fat'h Al-Bari*

3. *Al-Tibb An-Nabawi*

4. *'Ilm Al-Adwiyah*

5. *Al-Tibb An-Nabawi Wal-'Ilm Al-Hadith* by An-Naseemi

6. *Al-Tibb Min Al-Qur'an Wal-Sunnah* by Al-Baghdadi.

*****

Al-Khamr (Alcohol)

Al-Khamr in Arabic language refers to something that intoxicates. It is so called because it befogs the mind (*Tukhamir Al-'Aql*).

In the terminology of the *Shari'ah*, *Al-Khamr* refers to anything that intoxicates in large or small quantities, whether it is made from grapes, dates, wheat, barley or anything else, based on the words of the Prophet, peace and blessings of Allah be upon him: "Every intoxicant is Khamr, and all Khamr is Haram." (Narrated by Muslim)

Allah, the Exalted, says (interpretation of the meaning):

﴿ يَٰٓأَيُّهَا ٱلَّذِينَ ءَامَنُوٓا۟ إِنَّمَا ٱلۡخَمۡرُ وَٱلۡمَيۡسِرُ وَٱلۡأَنصَابُ وَٱلۡأَزۡلَٰمُ رِجۡسٌ مِّنۡ عَمَلِ ٱلشَّيۡطَٰنِ فَٱجۡتَنِبُوهُ لَعَلَّكُمۡ تُفۡلِحُونَ ﴾

"O you who believe! Intoxicants (all kinds of alcoholic drinks), and gambling, and Al-Ansab (stone altars for sacrifices to idols, etc.), and Al-Azlam (arrows for seeking luck or decision) are an abomination of Shaitan's handiwork. So avoid (strictly all) that (abomination) in order that you may be successful." (Soorah Al-Ma'idah, 5:90)

Some heedless people think that the word "avoid" means that it is *Makrooh* (disliked) and not *Haram* (forbidden), even though avoiding means it is more emphatically forbidden than if Allah, Most High, had said, "do not drink it," because saying "do not drink it" would mean that it is permissible to keep it, give it, sell it or sit at a table where alcohol is being drunk; all that would matter is not drinking it! But "avoiding" means that all of that is definitively forbidden.

Hence, the fact that alcohol is *Haram* is proved by the Book of Allah, the *Sunnah* of His Prophet and the consensus of the *Ummah*.

This is proved by the words of the Qur'an:

$$﴿ إِنَّمَا يُرِيدُ ٱلشَّيْطَـٰنُ أَن يُوقِعَ بَيْنَكُمُ ٱلْعَدَاوَةَ وَٱلْبَغْضَآءَ$$
$$فِي ٱلْخَمْرِ وَٱلْمَيْسِرِ وَيَصُدَّكُمْ عَن ذِكْرِ ٱللَّهِ وَعَنِ ٱلصَّلَوٰةِ فَهَلْ أَنتُم مُّنتَهُونَ ﴾$$

"Shaitan (Satan) wants only to excite enmity and hatred between you with intoxicants (alcoholic drinks) and gambling, and hinder you from the remembrance of Allah and from As-Salah (the prayer). So, will you not then abstain?" (Soorah Al-Ma'idah, 5:91)

The prohibition on alcohol was introduced gradually, in response to several incidents, because pre-Islamic Arabs were very fond of drinking it.

The first Verses to be revealed discouraged it, as Allah, the Exalted, said:

$$﴿ يَسْـَٔلُونَكَ عَنِ ٱلْخَمْرِ وَٱلْمَيْسِرِ قُلْ فِيهِمَآ$$
$$إِثْمٌ كَبِيرٌ وَمَنَـٰفِعُ لِلنَّاسِ وَإِثْمُهُمَآ أَكْبَرُ مِن نَّفْعِهِمَا ﴾$$

"They ask you (O Muhammad ﷺ) concerning alcoholic drink and gambling. Say: 'In them is a major sin, and (some) benefits for men, but the sin of them is bigger than their benefit'..." (Soorah Al-Baqarah, 2:219)

When this Verse was revealed, some of the people gave it up, and said, "We have no need of that in which there is major sin." But others did not give it up. They said, "We will take its benefits and leave its sin." Then this Verse was revealed:

﴿ يَـٰٓأَيُّهَا ٱلَّذِينَ ءَامَنُوا۟ لَا تَقْرَبُوا۟ ٱلصَّلَوٰةَ وَأَنتُمْ سُكَـٰرَىٰ حَتَّىٰ تَعْلَمُوا۟ مَا تَقُولُونَ ﴾

"O you who believe! Approach not As-Salah (the prayer) when you are in a drunken state until you know (the meaning) of what you utter..." (Soorah An-Nisa', 4:43)

Then some people gave it up and said, "We have no need of that which will distract us from prayer." But some others drank it at times other than the times of prayer, until Allah, the Exalted, revealed the Verse:

﴿ يَـٰٓأَيُّهَا ٱلَّذِينَ ءَامَنُوٓا۟ إِنَّمَا ٱلْخَمْرُ وَٱلْمَيْسِرُ وَٱلْأَنصَابُ
وَٱلْأَزْلَـٰمُ رِجْسٌ مِّنْ عَمَلِ ٱلشَّيْطَـٰنِ فَٱجْتَنِبُوهُ لَعَلَّكُمْ تُفْلِحُونَ ﴾

"O you who believe! Intoxicants (all kinds of alcoholic drinks), and gambling, and Al-Ansab (stone altars for sacrifices to idols, etc.), and Al-Azlam (arrows for seeking luck or decision) are an abomination of Shaitan's handiwork. So avoid (strictly all) that (abomination) in order that you may be successful." (Soorah Al-Ma'idah, 5:90)

Then it became *Haram* for them, until some of them said, "Allah has not forbidden anything worse than Khamr."

The prohibition of alcohol and gambling is emphasized in several ways:

- The sentence which refers to intoxicants and gambling starts with the word *Innama*, meaning "indeed" or "verily".

- Allah mentions them alongside idol-worship.

- He describes them as *Rijs* (an abomination).

- He describes them as the handiwork of *Shaitan*, and the *Shaitan* does nothing but pure evil.

- He commands us to avoid them.

- He describes such avoidance as part of success, and if avoiding them is success then doing them is loss and destruction.

- He mentions the calamities to which they lead to hostility and hatred among those who drink and gamble, and how they lead to keeping away from the remembrance Allah, the Exalted, and paying attention to the prayer times. The words "So, will you not then abstain?" are a most eloquent way of forbidding it. It is like saying: Many reasons to avoid it have been mentioned to you; will you not then stop, or will you continue as if you had never received this exhortation?

Sunnah

There are many narrations which speak of the prohibition on *Khamr*, such as the following:

Ibn Mas'ood, may Allah be pleased with him, said concerning intoxicants: "Allah has not put your healing in that which He has forbidden to you." (Narrated by Al-Bukhari. It was also narrated by Al-Tabarani in a *Marfoo'* report)

It was narrated from Wa'il Al-Hadrami that Tariq Ibn Suwayd Al-Ju'fi asked the Prophet, peace and blessings of Allah be upon him, about *Khamr*. He told him not to make it or he disapproved of him making it. He said, "We only use it as a remedy." The Prophet, peace and blessings of Allah be upon him, said: "It is not a remedy; rather it is a disease." (Narrated by Muslim)

According to a version narrated by Ahmad: "It is a disease and it is not a remedy."

Ruling on one who regards drinking Khamr as permissible

The one who regards it as permissible is a *Kafir* and apostate whose blood and wealth are permissible (subject to a ruling issued by a court under *Shari'ah*).

Punishment for the one who drinks it

The *Hadd* punishment for the one who drinks *Khamr* is proved in the *Sunnah* and there are many narrations about the punishment for the drinker of *Khamr*. For example it was narrated from Anas, may Allah be pleased with him, that a man who had drunk *Khamr* was brought to the Prophet, peace and blessings of Allah be upon him, and he had him whipped with palm branches forty times. He (Anas) said, "And Abu Bakr did likewise." When 'Umar, may Allah be pleased with him, became Caliph, he consulted the people and 'Abdur Rahman, may Allah be pleased with him, said, "The lightest of Hadd punishments is eighty (lashes), so 'Umar enjoined that." (Narrated by Muslim)

It was narrated that Al-Sa'ib Ibn Yazeed, may Allah be pleased with him, said, "The drinker (of Khamr) would be brought to us at the time of the Messenger of Allah, peace and blessings of Allah be upon him, and Abu Bakr, may Allah be pleased with him, and the first part of the caliphate of 'Umar, may Allah be pleased with him, and we would carry out the punishment with our hands, shoes and cloaks, and the punishment remained forty lashes until, toward the end of 'Umar's Caliphate, when they persisted and disobeyed, he made it eighty

lashes. (Narrated by Al-Bukhari)

The Companions and those who came after them were unanimously agreed that the one who drinks *Khamr* is to be flogged, but they differed as to the number of lashes – forty or eighty. The majority are of the view that it should be eighty.

Based on that, according to the majority, the drinker is to be given the *Hadd* punishment regardless of whether he becomes drunk or not, and this applies to the one who drinks any intoxicant, whether he drinks a lot or a little. What is mentioned in Hanafi *Fatwas* is that the one who consumes *Khamr*, whether a little or a lot, is to be punished.

Ruling on benefiting from Khamr

The majority of Muslim jurists are of the view that it is *Haram* (impermissible) to benefit from *Khamr* for medicinal purposes or otherwise, such as using it on the skin, or as food or in making clay.

They quote as evidence the words of Ibn Mas'ood, may Allah be pleased with him, as narrated by Al-Bukhari, "Allah has not put your healing in that which He has forbidden to you." (Narrated by Al-Bukhari; It was also narrated by Al-Tabarani in a *Marfoo'* report)

And Muslim narrated in his *Saheeh* from Wa'il Al-Hadrami that Tariq Ibn Suwayd Al-Ju'fi asked the Prophet, peace and blessings of Allah be upon him, about *Khamr*. He told him not to make it or he disapproved of him making it. He said, "We only use it as a remedy." The Prophet, peace and blessings of Allah be upon him, said, "It is not a remedy; rather it is a disease." (Narrated by Muslim)

According to a version narrated by Ahmad, "It is a disease and it is not a remedy."

The majority said that the one who drinks it for medicinal purposes is to be given the *Hadd* punishment. The Shaf'is are of the view that using *Khamr* as medicine is *Haram* according to the more correct view if it is pure and not mixed with anything else in which it is dissolved, and the *Hadd* punishment must be given in that case. But if it is mixed with something else in which it is dissolved, then it is permissible to use it as medicine if nothing else that is *Tahir* (pure) is available that can be used as medicine instead. In that case the principle of necessity in

Islamic jurisprudence applies.

Imam An-Nawawi, may Allah have Mercy upon him, was of the view that it is definitely *Haram* and said, "The correct view is that it is *Haram* to use *Khamr* for medicinal purposes."

The Problem of Alcohol in the World

Alcohol is one of the most complex problems that the West is suffering from and is looking for a solution, but with no success. American Sen. William Fulbright says of the alcohol problem, "We have reached the moon but our feet are still sinking in the mud. It is a real problem when we realize that in the United States there are more than 11 million alcoholics and more than 44 million drinkers."

The British scientific journal, *The Lancet*, published an article entitled *"Craving Alcohol"* in which it says, "If you are craving alcohol then you will certainly die because of it."

More than 200,000 people die every year in Britain because of alcohol.

According to estimates, 93 percent of the inhabitants of the United States drink alcohol and 40 percent of men suffer from temporary sickness because of it, while 5 percent of women and 10 percent of men suffer from chronic illnesses because of it.

Toxic effects of alcohol

Does the drinker know that alcohol is a deadly poison?

Before drinking, the one who makes alcohol can inhale its fumes, which leads to the development of a reaction in his bronchial tubes and lungs, and in the lining of the nose, which results in weakening of the sense of smell. Thus, the meaning of the words of Allah, the Exalted, becomes clear, "avoid (strictly all) that". It is a prohibition against coming near it at all, and this is more general than a prohibition on drinking it.

The toxic effects of alcohol vary according to its level in the blood. When it reaches a level of 20-99 milligrams percent it causes a change in mood, lack of coordination and confusion. At a level of 100-299

milligrams percent in the blood, it causes nausea, blurred vision and lack of balance. At a level of 300-399 milligrams percent, body temperature falls, speech becomes slurred and there is loss of memory. At a level of 400-700 milligrams percent the person falls into a state of deep unconsciousness with shallow breathing that may even result in death.

Despite the fact that all parts of the body are affected by alcohol, the nervous system is most severely affected, as the areas of the brain that control the most complex tasks are suppressed, and the cortex of the brain loses its ability to analyze information. It also affects the breathing centers in the brain and increased intake of alcohol slows them down completely and may lead to death.

The book *Alcoholism* confirms that after alcohol is absorbed in the intestine and reaches the blood, it is able to cross the cerebral membrane and also reach the fetus via the placenta. It is able to reach all tissues but it accumulates especially in fatty tissues. The more complex and specialized the tissue's function, the greater its risk of succumbing to the toxic effects of alcohol.

No wonder, then, that we see that the brain, liver and endocrine glands are the first to succumb to the effects of alcohol, which has a dangerous effect on them.

Effects of alcohol on the digestive system

The passage of alcohol through the mouth leads to infections and fissures on the tongue, and the sense of taste becomes confused as a result of the taste buds shrinking. The tongue dries up and the person may begin to drool in an off-putting manner. When addiction develops, a white layer forms on the tongue which is regarded as a preliminary stage to cancer of the tongue. The *Medicine* magazine confirms that addiction is often accompanied by infection of the parotid gland (a salivary gland).

Alcohol causes dilation of the veins in the mucous layer of the oesophagus, which may cause ulcers and severe bleeding, which may in turn cause the addict to vomit a lot of blood.

It has been proved that 90 percent of those who suffer from cancer of the oesophagus are alcoholics.

In the stomach, the mucous lining becomes swollen and secretions of hydrochloric acid and pepsin increase, which leads to stomach ulcers and bleeding. In alcoholics the stomach may be affected by infection and chronic atrophy, leading to cancer of the stomach which is very rare in individuals who do not drink alcohol.

Peristalsis is interrupted in those who drink to excess; they also suffer chronic stomach infections and diarrhea, a great deal of wind, and difficulty in absorbing nutrients.

The liver – an important victim of alcohol

The liver performs important functions in the body. It is a storehouse for all nutrients, and it controls the level of toxins and produces bile.

Alcohol is very toxic to liver cells, and getting rid of alcohol distracts the liver from its vital functions; dangerous developments result in the liver from alcohol addiction.

In France alone, more than 22,000 people die annually as a result

of alcoholic cirrhosis of the liver. In Germany, approximately 16,000 people die as alcohol is burned in the liver, which leads to the addict being disinclined to eat, which in turn leads to malnutrition.

The liver grows fatty as the result of burning alcohol, and it becomes enlarged and painful.

- **Alcoholic Hepatitis**: This is a temporary problem that results from staying up and drinking. Its symptoms include abdominal pain, vomiting, fever, tiredness and enlargement of the liver.

- **Cirrhosis of the liver**: This involves widespread destruction of liver cells, in which its tissue becomes fibrous, the liver becomes hard and small, and unable to perform its functions.

The patient complains of pain in the liver region, loss of appetite, loss of weight, nausea and vomiting and then he is affected by jaundice. It may also be accompanied by infection in the brain, lethargy or haemorrhage in the oesophagus, any of which may be fatal.

Effects of alcohol on the heart

The alcoholic may be affected by a number of serious and fatal disorders that affect the heart, such as:

- Weakness of the heart muscle, where the heart becomes sluggish, leading to difficulty in breathing, overall weakness, irregular heartbeat, enlargement of the liver and swelling of the feet, and the patient may die if he is not prevented from drinking alcohol.

- Blood pressure may rise as a result of addiction.

- Coronary artery disease: alcohol leads to hardening and narrowing of the veins of the heart, which manifests itself in angina pectoris.

- Irregular heartbeat

Effects of alcohol on the nervous system

Nerve cells are regarded as most vulnerable to the toxic effects of alcohol, which has an immediate effect on the brain, some of which is temporary and some is irreparable. Research has confirmed that

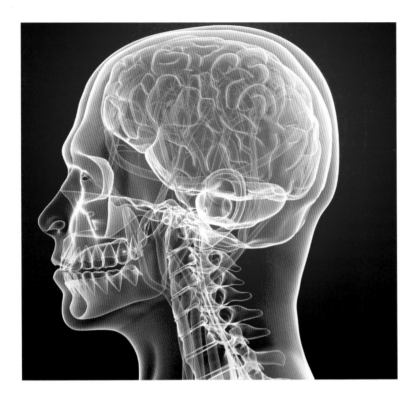

drinking just one or two cups of alcohol may cause some brain cells to die. Hence, we can see the miraculous nature of the Prophet's words: "That which intoxicates in large amounts, a little of it is *Haram*."

The cerebral cortex of the addict may be affected, which causes the alcoholic to complain of headache and nervous agitation, and may end up in complete unconsciousness. The nerves are also susceptible to damage caused by alcohol.

Harm to the brain may manifest itself in the form of some kinds of epilepsy, which manifests itself in some alcoholics in the form of fainting attacks and convulsions.

Effects of alcohol on sexual function

Arab literature tells the story of a Bedouin woman who was made drunk by some people in the era of *Jahiliyyah* (ignorance). When she began to feel strange, she said, "Do your womenfolk drink this?" They

said, "Yes". She said, "If you are telling the truth, then not one of you knows who his father is."

Doctors say that alcohol increases female libido thus making her sexual behavior reckless. It comes as no surprise that a woman's first sexual experience may come when she is under the influence of alcohol, and it has been confirmed that most cases of unmarried pregnancy occur as the result of drunken behavior.

The female alcoholic's menstrual cycle may become irregular and she may reach menopause ten years before her peers. Her ovaries may also suffer damage.

In the case of men, despite the fact that libido increases in the early stages of drinking, the addict's ability to perform sexually decreases until a state of complete impotence is reached.

Alcohol damages reproductive cells, which leads to atrophy of the testicles. Before that, there may be deformed sperm which leads to deformed fetuses.

Alcohol weakens the immune system

The body's ability to resist disease is weakened in the case of addicts, especially resistance to tuberculosis and so on.

This was formerly regarded as a result of malnourishment, but recent research has proved that weakening of the immune system in alcoholics is the result of the direct impact of alcohol on the immune system.

Serious effects of alcohol on offspring

Dr. Ahmad Shawkat Al-Shatti says, "The marriage of two alcoholics is a serious matter, because the husband who is dead set on drinking is not fit to be a husband, and his offspring will inherit from him a sickly constitution. This is known as fetal alcohol syndrome, which refers to what happens to the offspring of alcoholics, making them physically and psychologically weak. It has been proved that alcohol passes from the mother to the fetus via the placenta and affects it; alcohol may also be transmitted to the infant vas breast milk."

References:

1. *Rawai' Al-Tibb An-Nabawi* by Dr. Muhammad Nizar Al-Daqar
2. *Nazarat Fil-Musakkirat* by Dr. Ahmad Shawkat Al-Shatti

✳✳✳✳✳

Analytical Look at Alcohol

A brief look at a field study
encompassing 50,000 people

By Dr. 'Umar Al-Baqir Saleh (Sudan)

Global health statistics about alcohol and its effects show that the causes of death resulting from drinking alcohol and everything that stems from that occupy a prominent place in the list of causes of death in the United States, France and many other countries.

One-third of hospital beds in industrialized countries are occupied by patients whose ailment is connected to alcohol. The Texas government has published statistics showing that what is spent on treating drinkers, in addition to the economic losses that result from loss of property, compensation payments and loss of productivity is many times greater than the profits of selling alcohol. This is the case in most countries in the modern world.

The first question is: How can this disease have dogged mankind from the dawn of history until our own times, destroying individuals and societies, without man being able to defeat and overcome it as he has with so many other diseases?

Answering this question needs many books and volumes, but I will try to shed light on the nature of this treacherous disease that has enabled it to remain until the present day, and I will explain the reasons why this eternal problem has continued.

• The brief euphoria and happy feeling that occur with the first few glasses of alcohol.

Science has proved that this happy feeling is no more than an illusion. Alcohol is not a stimulant; it is a narcotic. Science has shown the real nature of this treacherous euphoria, which is as follows: It is well-known that man's brain has a center which is formed of a number of sensitive cells which control whatever impulses come from the primitive center of the brain and refine them in a manner that befits a human and enables life to continue. When a person consumes alcohol, these sensitive cells are suppressed and no longer able to function. Thus the primitive center is unleashed which is manifest in actions without inhibitions or restraints. This is the reason why you see some of those who are renowned for being quiet or shy by day becoming loquacious after drinking alcohol; the stocky, staid person will take to the dance floor and shake his body as if he was a member of a professional group; and the person with a husky voice will start singing.

But when the number of glasses consumed increases, other centers of the brain start to slow down, one after another, and the person starts to stumble, talk a lot, urinate a lot and may fall asleep, slumped over on a chair.

• As human societies started to become increasingly aware, they began to realize the harmful social, economic and health-related effects of alcohol, and human society feels frustrated by this problem.

Many scientists have competed in producing a definition of this word and their opinions may be summed up as follows: "Alcohol does

not become harmful unless the person continually consumes it in large quantities, and becomes mentally and physically dependent on it, which leads to physical, economic and social damage."

This definition may give free rein to anyone who does not match this description to continue drinking alcohol. But different research has explained the shallowness and danger of this view. An in-depth examination of the situation clearly shows the harmful effect that alcohol has, as it is able to change people's behavior and way of thinking to such an extent that it has become firmly entrenched, as if society does not want to get rid of it.

The next stage

Astounding scientific studies have disproved this definition of alcoholism and pointed out the real problem. The number of alcoholics among those who drink is no more than three percent, so naturally they are not responsible for most of the damage caused to society such as the rise in the divorce rate, the breakup of families, traffic accidents, and fall in productivity, because their state of physical health renders them incapable of being involved in such activities.

So who is responsible? The real danger comes from that class which drinks daily or on special occasions, even if they are not called alcoholics.

It has become clear that a small amount of alcohol is harmful to man and leads to the death of brain cells.

Dr. Melvin Kinsley, a professor of anatomy in the Carolina Medical College in USA, along with his colleagues, has proved that a single glass of alcohol leads to the death of one brain cell, and it is well-known that this cell will not grow again. This harmful effect increases every time a person drinks, killing more of these cells.

This discovery is regarded as one of the greatest discoveries made by science in modern times; it has clarified the matter and demolished forever the theory that drinking alcohol in small amounts is not harmful. Here we should mention the wisdom of Islam that is represented in the words of the Prophet, peace and blessings of Allah be upon him, as narrated by An-Nasa'i and At-Tirmidhi: "Whatever intoxicates in large amounts, a small amount of it is *Haram*."

According to another report by An-Nasa'i: "I forbid you to consume small amounts of that which intoxicates in large amounts."

And according to a third report narrated by An-Nasa'i: The Prophet, peace and blessings of Allah be upon him, forbade a small amount of that which intoxicates in large amounts.

Alcohol is killing more Russians

A health report in Russia states that the number of Russians who have died of alcohol poisoning has increased by 30 percent when compared to the same period last year. A representative of the Russian Ministry of Health, Genady Onshintishenko, explained, in a statement to the ITAR-Tass Russian news agency, that these figures reflect an increased desire among Russians for alcoholic drinks, especially among men, and also point to the bad quality of the alcohol consumed.

The Russian official added that the matter does not have to do only with those who are addicted to alcohol; rather it has primarily to do with ordinary Russian citizens who drink alcohol regularly.

However, the Russian agency did not state the numbers of cases of death that had to do with addiction, or with the low quality of the alcohol that is available, or the issue of adulteration.

The report indicates that the number of deaths caused by alcohol poisoning increased by an average of four thousand, reaching a total of more than 16,800.

Lethal doses

Alcohol is regarded as relatively cheap in Russia, as the price of a 2-liter bottle of gin mixed with tonic water is approximately $1.70.

But most Russians prefer to buy vodka, which is stronger, or other kinds of alcohol that are produced domestically, but which in many cases contain contaminants that may be lethal.

The Russian official stated that there are nearly two million Russians who are classified as alcoholics, including 56,000 children who are not older than 14 years. He stated that the Russian man's average annual consumption of alcohol is no less than 14 liters.

Treating Sickness with Alcohol

Dr. Muhammad 'Ali Al-Barr
Kingdom of Saudi Arabia

Is alcohol a medicine or is it a poison? Dr. Aubrey Lewis, the head of the Institute of Psychiatry of the University of London, said in the most famous medical reference book in Britain, *Price Medical Reference*, 10th edition: "Alcohol is the only legal poison. It is sold worldwide and everyone who wants to escape his problems will find it available to him. Hence, it is drunk a great deal by those with disordered personalities, which leads to psychopathic anomaly. A single dose of alcohol may cause poisoning and lead to either euphoria or immobility, and may lead to unconsciousness. Those who are addicted to drinking alcohol (alcoholics) may become completely promiscuous and insane."

During the time of the Messenger of Allah, peace and blessings of Allah be upon him, and after that, until recently, doctors claimed that there were some medicinal benefits in alcohol, but with the advance of scientific discoveries these claims were proved false. It became clear that these were mere illusions and that the words of the Prophet, peace and blessings of Allah be upon him, were the ultimate truth about which there was no doubt or confusion. Prophet Muhammad, peace and blessings of Allah be upon him, said concerning alcohol, when Tariq Al-Ju'fi, may Allah be pleased with him, asked him about it, not to use it. Tariq said, "I only prescribe it as a remedy". The Prophet, peace and blessings of Allah be upon him, said: "It is not a remedy; rather it is a disease." (Narrated by Muslim and Al-Tirmidhi)

It was narrated from Abu Hurairah, may Allah be pleased with him, that the Messenger of Allah, peace and blessings of Allah be upon him, forbade evil medicine. (Narrated by Abu Dawood)

Abu Dawood also narrated in his *Sunan* from Umm Al-Darda' that Abud-Darda' said, "The Messenger of Allah, peace and blessings of Allah be upon him, said 'Allah has sent down the disease and the remedy, and He has created for every disease a remedy, so treat sickness but do not treat it with anything that is *Haram*'."

In the past, some people were of the opinion that there were some medicinal benefits in alcohol, and they quoted as evidence the words of Allah:

$$\text{﴿ يَسْـَٔلُونَكَ عَنِ ٱلْخَمْرِ وَٱلْمَيْسِرِ قُلْ فِيهِمَآ}$$
$$\text{إِثْمٌ كَبِيرٌ وَمَنَٰفِعُ لِلنَّاسِ وَإِثْمُهُمَآ أَكْبَرُ مِن نَّفْعِهِمَا ﴾}$$

"They ask you (O Muhammad ﷺ) concerning alcoholic drink and gambling. Say: 'In them is a major sin, and (some) benefits for men, but the sin of them is bigger than their benefit.'" (Soorah Al-Baqarah, 2:219)

But many *Imams* refuted this claim. Al-Ameer Al-San'ani said in his book, *Subul Al-Salam* and in *An-Najm Al-Wahhaj*:

"Everything that the doctors say about the benefits of *Khamr* and drinking it, because the Qur'an says that there are benefits for people in it, only applied before that was revealed. But after the revelation of this Verse:

$$\text{﴿ يَـٰٓأَيُّهَا ٱلَّذِينَ ءَامَنُوٓا إِنَّمَا ٱلْخَمْرُ وَٱلْمَيْسِرُ وَٱلْأَنصَابُ}$$
$$\text{وَٱلْأَزْلَٰمُ رِجْسٌ مِّنْ عَمَلِ ٱلشَّيْطَٰنِ فَٱجْتَنِبُوهُ لَعَلَّكُمْ تُفْلِحُونَ ﴾}$$

"O you who believe! Intoxicants (all kinds of alcoholic drinks), and gambling, and Al-Ansab (stone altars for sacrifices to idols, etc.), and Al-Azlam (arrows for seeking luck or decision) are an abomination of Shaitan's handiwork. So avoid (strictly all) that (abomination) in order that you may be successful." (Soorah Al-Ma'idah, 5:90)

Allah, the Creator of all things, took away all the benefits that were in it and now it contains nothing of benefit. Hence, the principle of treating disease with alcohol is baseless."

What he said was narrated from Al-Rabee' and Al-Dahhak. The benefits are imaginary; there may be financial gains for the one who sells alcohol and deals in it, but it causes a huge financial losses in society. As for the medical and industrial benefits, they are also imaginary, such as the belief that alcohol stimulates the appetite. Alcohol has been used to stimulate the appetite since ancient times. It was used by the Greeks, Romans, Persians and Arabs, who made it an art.

It is used by the Europeans today, especially the French, who call it aperitif. They usually do not eat heavy foods unless accompanied by alcohol, and the Italians do likewise.

Alcohol stimulates the appetite at first, so the secretion of stomach acid and hydrochloric acid increases, but after a while it causes irritation in the stomach, so this imaginary benefit is followed by harmful consequences, starting with irritation of the stomach lining, loss of appetite and repeated vomiting, and ending with cancer of the oesophagus.

Once, delegations from Yemen and Hadhramaut came to the Prophet, peace and blessings of Allah be upon him, and asked him to allow them to drink alcohol on the grounds that their land was cold, but he refused to allow them that.

Abu Dawood narrated that Daylam Al-Himiari said, "I said to the Messenger of Allah, 'O Messenger of Allah, I live in a cold land and we do hard work, and we have a drink made from wheat which we use to fortify ourselves for our hard work in our cold country.' He said: "Does it intoxicate?" I said, "Yes." He said: "Then avoid it." I said, "The people will not give it up." He said: "If they will not give it up, then fight them." (It is a *saheeh Hadith*)

More than fourteen hundred years after this incident, modern medicine tells us that this sense of warmth is no more than an illusion. Alcohol dilates the blood vessels, especially those that lie beneath the skin, so the person feels a false sense of warmth, as happens during Christmas in Europe and America, when many people get drunk and some of them stay out in the streets and parks, exposing themselves to the bitter cold, then some of them die of cold while enjoying that false sensation of warmth.

Another of these benefits is its use in industry as a preservative, a dehydrating agent and a solvent for some alkaline and fatty materials. It is also used as a skin cleanser and a solvent for some medicines that can only be dissolved in alcohol. It is also used as a solvent in perfumes and is used in the manufacture of scents and perfumes (such as cologne).

Its use as an antidote and medicine is disapproved in modern medicine, but it is still used as a solvent for some medicines and remedies. It is strange indeed that the scholars of Islam researched this issue thoroughly and came up with amazing studies. In *Mughni Al-*

Muhtaj it is said: Treating sickness with alcohol is *Haram* if it is pure and not mixed with anything else that dissolves in it. As for medicinal antidotes and the like which are dissolved in it, it is permissible to use them for medicinal purposes if there is no *Tahir* (pure) remedy available. In that case it comes under the ruling on medical treatment with *Najis* (impure) things, such as snake meat and urine. Similarly, it is permissible to use it for medicinal purposes in order to hasten recovery, provided that it is on the advice of a Muslim doctor of good character or of the one who has knowledge of that, and the amount used should be small and not cause intoxication.

There is no doubt about the prohibition of pure alcohol as a remedy, because it is a disease and is not a remedy. But using it as an antidote, and as it is now used in many medicines as a solvent for some alkaline and fatty substances which cannot be dissolved in water, is the kind of usage mentioned in *Mughni Al-Muhtaj*, and it is permissible subject to certain conditions:

- That there is no alcohol-free medicine that is available in this case
- That it is prescribed by a Muslim doctor of good character
- That the amount used should be small and should not cause intoxication

If we look at the alcohol-containing medicines that are available, we will see that they are of two types:

- The first type is alkaline or fatty substances that are used as medicine and can only be dissolved in alcohol.
- The second type is substances to which a little alcohol is added, not because of necessity but to give the syrup a special flavor and taste that the Europeans and Americans are used to, because this medicine comes to us readymade.

This second type is undoubtedly *Haram*, and the Muslim doctor should not rush to prescribe medicine which contains any alcohol; he should avoid them as much as possible.

None of the Muslim jurists *(Fuqaha')* permitted the use of alcohol as a medicine except in cases of extreme necessity, such as when a person has choked on food and can find nothing available except alcohol. In that case it is permissible to drink it with a view to removing the obstruction.

Sayyid Sabiq, may Allah have Mercy upon him, says in *Fiqh Al-Sunnah*, "The *Fuqaha'* gave the example of a person who chokes on food and is almost asphyxiated, and he cannot find anything to solve the problem except alcohol."

But Sayyid Sabiq made a serious mistake when he said, "Or he is about to die of cold and he cannot find anything to ward off death except a cup or dose of alcohol..." We have explained what is wrong with this notion that alcohol warms the body. He also made a mistake when he said, "Or the one who has a heart attack and nearly dies, and he knows because a doctor has told him that there is nothing to ward off this danger except a certain amount of alcohol..."

This is also a serious mistake and a fatal flaw, because alcohol does not dilate the coronary arteries that nourish the heart, as was previously imagined, rather it constricts them and creates fatty residues and cholesterol inside the arteries, thus it contributes to blockages, heart attacks and angina pectoris, especially if the person also smokes; both habits play a role in blocking the coronary arteries, accumulation of fatty residues and cholesterol, and constriction of the arteries.

Alcohol has another effect. It poisons the heart muscles (toxic cardiomyopathy). We say to Sheikh Sayyid Sabiq (may Allah forgive him) that it does not come under the heading of necessity which makes forbidden things permissible, as is imagined, rather it is a harmful effect which should be avoided.

Imam Ibn Al-Qayyim, may Allah have Mercy upon him, said something when he discussed this point in his book *Al-Tibb An-Nabawi*. His comments are of great significance and could not be overtaken by the claims of doctors of his own time that alcohol was a medicine; he explained how it is a disease. His faith in his Lord and His Messenger led him to the right conclusions, and he discovered things that were not known at his time; indeed he highlighted very subtle concepts which medicine did not discover until recently. One of these is the impact of believing in the remedy; if the sick person believes that the remedy is

good, then he may make some sort of recovery, whereas if he believes it is bad, he may not make any recovery.

This is called the placebo effect, which is known to all doctors. Ibn Al-Qayyim said, "Allah only forbade to this *Ummah* what He forbade because it is evil. His prohibition of it is a protection for them, which saves them from ingesting it, so it is not appropriate to seek healing from diseases and health problems through it. Even if they manage to remove the problem through it – according to the medicine of his time – it will result in more serious problems in the heart (i.e., in the spiritual sense), commensurate with the level of evil in the medicine. Thus, the one who prescribes it is trying to remove a physical problem in return for a problem in the heart (i.e., spiritual problems). The prohibition dictates avoiding it and keeping away from it in all possible ways, but using it as a remedy is encouraging people to deal with it. It is a disease as the Prophet, peace and blessings of Allah be upon him, said, so it is not permissible to use it as medicine. It gives attributes of evil to the physical body and the soul, because the nature of the body will clearly be affected by the way the medicine is applied or taken. So if the medicine has that impact because of the way in which it is taken, then how about if it is evil in and of itself? Hence, Allah forbade His slaves all food, drinks and clothing that are evil, because man's psyche will be impacted by this evil and its qualities."

He also added, "This issue is very subtle and has not yet been discovered in detail by medicine. After the digestion and absorption, food and drink turn into either energy that moves the body and fuel that feeds the brain and heart or building materials for the body, to replace that which is worn out with something new and good."

We now know that carbohydrates and fat turn into energy whereas proteins turn into cells and tissues; this happens by means of complex chemical processes.

The Krebs cycle, for example, is a number of highly complex chemical processes that turn blood sugar (glucose) in the mitochondria of cells into stored energy, involving approximately forty chemical processes. During the Krebs cycle and otherwise, a number of important amino acids are transformed to build cells and tissues. Protein is no more than a huge number of amino acids.

Hence, you can see that whatever you eat or drink changes to something that makes the muscles of your hand or heart move or give you energy to think, or it changes into the muscles themselves in the hand, tongue, or heart, or it flows through your veins with the blood, forming red or white blood cells, or platelets, or sperm that comes out of your loins. Does it not become part of your body or help to form

your ideas, after you eat and drink evil things such as alcohol, pork and other things that Allah has forbidden? Indeed it is so.

Are not the words of Ibn Al-Qayyim very subtle and brilliant, when they discuss something that modern science has not paid any attention to even today? Indeed it is so.

As Ibn Al-Qayyim, may Allah have Mercy upon him, said, "It gives the quality of evil to the body and soul. Everything that is eaten or drunk enters the body and flows through the veins with the blood, either by means of catabolism, whereby it is turned into energy, or by building whereby it turns into cells and tissue."

If the evil substance enters the stomach of the son of Adam and flows through his veins, then that evil is the source of the energy used by his

hand, tongue, brain and heart. Evil becomes a part of the muscles in his body and of the cells of his blood or his sperm that comes out of his loins and evil undoubtedly affects everything.

This confirms what Ibn Al-Qayyim said, "Hence, Allah has forbidden to His slaves (certain) food, drink and clothing, because the quality of evil has an impact on the person."

Then Ibn Al-Qayyim said, "It is known that the Muslim belief that this substance (*Khamr*) is *Haram* (forbidden in Islam) and creates a barrier that prevents him from believing that it is a blessing and beneficial, or thinking positively of it and consuming it. Rather the greater a person's faith, the more he will hate it and think badly of it, and he will naturally be put off by it. If he consumes it in that case, it will be a disease, not a cure."

These are amazing words, and medical research nowadays is adopting this line of thought. This is the difference in the impact that a medicine has in different societies. When a certain medicine has a certain impact in one society, it will be different, if only slightly, in another society. Indeed, the effect of a medicine may differ from one person to another. Many different factors play a role, not the least of which are psychological factors in the person who is taking the medicine. If he is taking the medicine willingly and believes that it is beneficial, he will have experience sort of healing, but if he is taking it unwillingly and thinks badly of it, or thinks that it is harmful, then he will not experience any kind of healing and may even experience some kind of harm. This is a new field in medicine. Ibn Al-Qayyim understood the psychological aspect of taking medicine but this is something that is not clearly understood even today, and research is still being carried out in this field.

With regard to the effect of evil medicine, food or drink on one's offspring, this is also a new area of medicine. A lot has been said about it after the Thalidomide story, which was a sedative drug that was believed to be free of complications, but when it was given to pregnant women, it affected the fetus and children were born without limbs. Many cases appeared before the courts, especially in Germany where this drug was invented. It was eventually withdrawn, but the company went bankrupt because it was forced to pay too many penalties and compensation payments.

It has become clear that the children of alcoholics are usually addicted too and there is often an inclination toward crime, as well as a prevalence of mental illness, feeble-mindedness and insanity.

But does all of that result from the effect of alcohol on the chromosomes and genes which carry the DNA in the father's sperm or the mother's egg, or is it the result of a bad environment?

Scientists answer this by saying: We could not find any gene in the sperm or egg that causes addiction, but we know that the rate of addiction is very high in those who have a family history of addiction (62 percent), whereas among ordinary drinkers (social drinkers) the rate is low (16 percent), as stated by a team of doctors, who treat addiction in the United States.

Other experiments were also carried out in which the children of addicts were removed from their families and given a regular upbringing far away from addiction. It was found that a large percentage of them turned to addiction when they were exposed to drinking. This indicates that there is at least a hereditary predisposition toward addiction among addicts, and that drinking alcohol leads to the creation of sperm in the man or eggs in the woman that are affected in one of the genes, giving the potential to drink alcohol to the point of addiction. In brief, as Dr. Lincoln Williams says in his book *Alcoholism Explained*, the seed of addiction grows fast in the soil of addictive families.

Thus hereditary factors are combined with environmental factors to create offspring who are inclined toward addiction, i.e., as soon as they drink alcohol they do not have the ability to stop as most drinkers do, rather they continue drinking until they are drunk.

Before we finish this chapter about using alcohol as medicine, we would like to tell of some incidents which point to the depth of faith and how the Muslims responded to the words of Allah and His Messenger, peace and blessings be upon him, with complete obedience and did not believe the views of the doctors of their time. Then science progressed and medicine advanced, and we see that modern doctors are discovering the truth of the Muslims' stance, and the falseness of what the doctors of that time believed. We have already quoted the

words of Ibn Al-Qayyim concerning this matter. He said these words at a time when all doctors were unanimously agreed that alcohol was a remedy, but because of the sincerity of his faith, he refused to believe that myth. Now we will look at that which was narrated from Imam Ja'afar As-Sadiq, may Allah have Mercy upon him, concerning this matter:

Someone asked Imam Ja'afar about a man who had a severe case of haemorrhoids and a medicine made of *Nabeedh* (a kind of alcohol) was prescribed for him, not for the sake of pleasure but as a remedy. He said, "No, not even one sip." He was asked, "Why?" He said, "Because it is *Haram* and Allah has not put any cure or healing in that which He has forbidden."

In the medicine of past, it was thought that the remedy for haemorrhoids was alcohol, and at that time doctors did not realize that alcohol causes haemorrhoids and aggravates them in two ways:

- Directly, because of the expansion and swelling that it causes in the blood vessels of the anus
- By means of cirrhosis of the liver and increasing blood pressure in the hepatic portal vein

One of them said to Imam Ja'afar Sadiq, may Allah have Mercy upon him, "I have pain, and drink *Nabeedh* which was prescribed to me by the doctor." He said, "What is preventing you from drinking water from which Allah created every living thing?" He said, "It does not suit me."

He said, "What is preventing you from eating honey in which Allah says there is healing for people?" He said, "I do not find it."

He said, "What is preventing you from drinking milk from which your flesh grew and your bones got strong?" He said, "It does not suit me."

He said, "You want me to tell you to drink alcohol but by Allah I will not tell you to do that."

As-Sadiq was asked about medicine that is mixed with alcohol. He said, "I would not like to look at it or smell it, so how could I take it?"

The British magazine, *The Lancet*, which is one of the most famous medical magazines in the world, published an article in 1987 entitled "Craving Alcohol". The author started his article by saying, "If you crave alcohol then you will surely die because of it."

He mentioned that 200,000 people die every year in England because of alcohol.

The Royal College of Internists, Psychologists and Practitioners published reports which all agreed on the danger of alcohol and that alcohol does not leave any part of the body unaffected. In the book *Alcoholism* there is a list of diseases that result from drinking alcohol, including diseases of the mouth, throat, oesophagus, stomach and intestines; alcoholic liver disease and cirrhosis; and pancreatic disease. Then it says:

The effects of alcohol appear immediately in the brain; some of these effects are temporary and some are irreversible. If a person drinks one or two glasses of any kind of alcohol, it may cause some of the brain cells to die, and if the drinker continues to consume intoxicants, then he may be affected by what is called Wernicke-Korsakoff syndrome, in which the patient looks scared and starts to mumble, and his eyes move constantly or his eye muscles may be paralyzed. The patient loses the ability to retain information. When the drinker is affected in this way, the possibility of recovery is very unlikely. Alcohol also affects the muscles of the heart and leads to high blood pressure and coronary disease.

It has been scientifically proved that alcohol is connected to cancer of the mouth, oesophagus, throat and liver. Scientific studies have proved that alcohol is a carcinogen and may also cause deformities in the fetuses of mothers who drink alcohol.

All of that confirms the miraculous nature of the words of the Prophet, peace and blessings of Allah be upon him: "It is not a remedy; rather it is a disease."

(See *Qabasat Min Al-Tibb An-Nabawi*)

*****

AIDS

and the Prohibition on Fornication (*Zina*)

Islam is very keen to create a chaste and pure society in which desires are not provoked and sacred limits are not transgressed, so as to protect honor from being violated and lineages from becoming confused. So, Islam set out laws which guarantee that this sublime goal will be achieved; it enjoins *Hijab* and lowering the gaze, encourages marriage and prescribes *Hadd* punishments.

For this purpose there are warnings in the Book of Allah against abominations both apparent and hidden, and the narrations of the Prophet, peace and blessings of Allah be upon him, explain the consequences of the spread of blatant immorality among people. For example, the Prophet, peace and blessings of Allah be upon him, said: "Five things result from five: no people break the covenant but Allah will cause their enemy to prevail over them; they do not rule by something other than that which Allah has revealed but poverty will become widespread among them; immorality does not appear among them but death will become widespread among them; they do not cheat in weights and measures but they will be deprived of produce and be punished by drought; and they do not withhold *Zakah* but rain will be withheld from them." (Narrated by Al-Tabarani in *Al-Kabeer* from Ibn 'Abbas; it is a *hasan Hadith*)

According to a *Saheeh* report narrated by Ibn Majah, may Allah have Mercy upon him, "Immorality never appears among a people until they commit it openly, but the plague and sickness that did not exist among their predecessors in the past will become widespread among them."

Modern science and contemporary reality confirm the meaning of the *Hadith* and the Prophethood of Muhammad, peace and blessings of Allah be upon him, because mankind did not realize the truth of that until the last two decades of the twentieth century, during which immorality spread at an alarming rate and many sexually-transmitted diseases became common, which were not common before. All of that is because of the appearance and spread of immorality. First

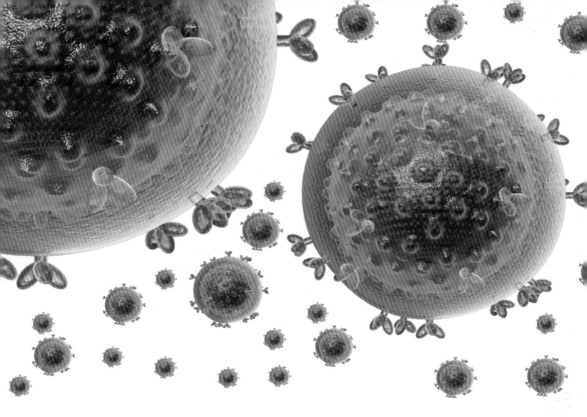

of all, syphilis appeared during the Franco-Italian War, when *Zina* (fornication) became widespread among the troops. The Italians called it the French disease.

When Western colonialists invaded Arab lands, they brought this disease with them, and at that time the Arabs called it *Al-da' Al-Franji* (the European disease), and this name is still used today.

In modern times, herpes appeared as a widespread sexually-transmitted disease, until the average number of people affected by this disease in the United States reached half a million cases.

In 1979, in the United States, Acquired Immune Deficiency Syndrome, which is known as AIDS, appeared for the first time. This is a virus which attacks the white blood cells that protect the human body, destroying them one after another until the body loses its most important means of defense, after which it becomes completely unable to resist diseases that the healthy body is able to defeat in ordinary circumstances. The patient remains like that until he dies after lengthy suffering and severe pain, which may be long or short, because of the collapse of the body's immune system.

This disease spread alarmingly among the homosexual community. At the beginning of 1981, the number of people affected by this disease was no more than a few dozen, but today the number has reached millions. Until now doctors have been unable to discover a treatment that can put an end to the AIDS virus. All they have managed to do is produce drugs that deal with the symptoms and reduce some of the more painful ones.

All of this is despite the fact that they have managed to put an end to a number of contagious diseases due to advances in medicine, but sexually-transmitted diseases are still among the most widespread contagious diseases in the world and the most difficult to treat.

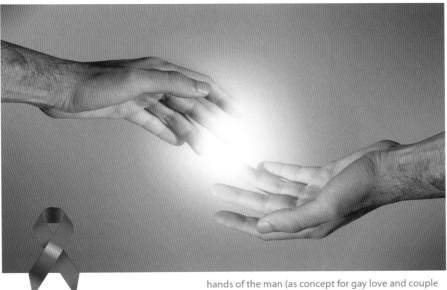

hands of the man (as concept for gay love and couple

In the *Merck Manual of Medicine* it says that sexually-transmitted diseases are among the most widely spread contagious diseases in the world, and the number of people infected is increasing annually. In the last two decades of the twentieth century, the World Health Organization (WHO) estimates that the number of people infected with gonorrhoea is more than 250 million annually, and the number of people infected with syphilis is estimated at 50 million annually. The

Atlanta Center for Fighting Contagious Disease in the state of Georgia in the US estimates that the number of people infected with gonorrhoea in the United States is three million people per year, and the number infected with syphilis is four hundred thousand per year.

In addition to the emergence of various other diseases because of the spread of immorality and homosexuality in permissive countries, all of that confirms the words of the Prophet, peace and blessings of Allah be upon him: "Immorality never appears among a people until they commit it openly, but the plague and sickness that did not exist among their predecessors in the past will become widespread among them."

﴿ وَٱللَّهُ غَالِبٌ عَلَىٰٓ أَمْرِهِۦ وَلَٰكِنَّ أَكْثَرَ ٱلنَّاسِ لَا يَعْلَمُونَ ﴾

"And Allah has full power and control over His affairs, but most of men know not." (Soorah Yoosuf, 12:21)

*****

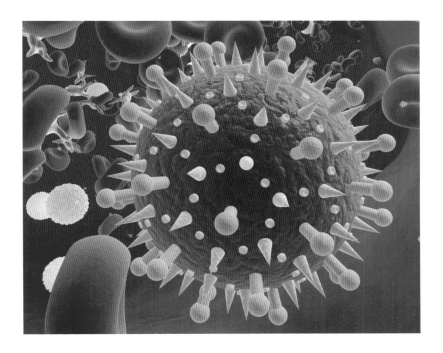

Sexually Transmitted Diseases

The subject of sexually-transmitted diseases is very important to doctors because of the serious danger to physical and mental health that it poses to individuals and societies. The greatest indication of global concern about these diseases was the huge conference that was held in America in 1974 to research syphilis and similar diseases. This conference was attended by fifteen hundred specialists from fifty countries, and their lectures were compiled in a large-format book of over five hundred pages.

The *Merck Medical Manual* (13th edition, 1977) states that diseases that are transmitted by illegitimate sexual relations (*Zina*) and homosexual relationships are the most widespread in the world today. The number of those affected by these diseases increases

every year, and that has been the case for nearly two decades. The World Health Organization estimates that the number of people infected with gonorrhoea is more than 150,000 every year, and the number of those infected with syphilis, which is known in some Arab countries as the "European disease", is more than fifty thousand every year.

The Atlanta Center for Fighting Infectious Diseases in the state of Georgia in the US estimates the number of people in the United States infected with gonorrhoea as three million, and the number of those infected with syphilis at four hundred thousand. That was in 1976. The *Graduate Doctor* magazine (May 1983 edition) and the American *Time* magazine (July 1983 edition) state that twenty million Americans suffer from the venereal disease herpes, and half a million new cases are diagnosed annually in the United States. In Britain, 15,000 new cases were diagnosed in 1982.

Despite the in-depth research and the huge amount of money spent on treating sexually-transmitted disease in the West, it is becoming more widespread every day due to the increase in sexual perversion.

The danger of these sexually transmitted diseases is that they spread quickly from a sick person to a healthy one. Some of them are transmitted via sexual contact, and some are transmitted via kissing a carrier of the disease, and some by touching or using personal items that belong to the sick person.

In the following lines I will focus on four diseases that are widespread, namely: gonorrhoea, syphilis, herpes and AIDS, and some other diseases. For information on that I referred to a number of books on sexually-transmitted diseases and medical magazines. These diseases are as follows:

Gonorrhoea

Gonorrhoea is a widespread sexually-transmitted disease that spreads easily and appears 3-7 days after the first contact with an infected person.

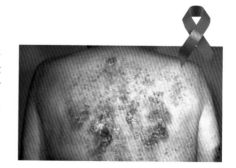

The symptoms of gonorrhoea

in men are painful secretions and a burning sensation when urinating. In women, it leads to some secretions. If gonorrhoea is not treated fully to destroy the germs, then after a while it may appear in other places and cause complications. It may cause sterility in women, infection in the joints and irregular heartbeat. Gonorrhoea is one of the most widespread diseases because it spreads quickly and easily.

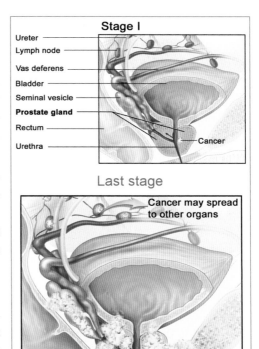

How infection happens

Gonorrhoea is transmitted via sexual contact and in rare cases by sitting on contaminated toilet seats or using towels, sponges, thermometers or other things that may carry living germs by touching or direct contact.

Symptoms of gonorrhoea

The symptoms usually appear first in the urethra, when a burning sensation is felt when passing urine; some patients complain of difficulty in urination. After twenty-four hours or more, the patient notices pus coming out of the urethra, which may be thick or viscous depending on the type of bacteria.

The first thing that the affected person notices is a discharge from the urethral opening or vagina, a rise in body temperature, headache and increased pulse.

After two weeks, pain on urination becomes worse and urination is interrupted, or the opposite may occur, with the symptoms decreasing to a level where they are not noticeable. The gonorrhoea bacteria may reach the circulatory system, leading to serious problems in the

heart, meninges or joints, or it may reach the epididymis or testicles. It cannot be determined with certainty that the patient is suffering from gonorrhoea until it is confirmed that the bacteria are present in the secretions or not. The absence of bacteria does not mean that the disease is not present, because they may appear later on, so it is essential to do repeated tests on consecutive days.

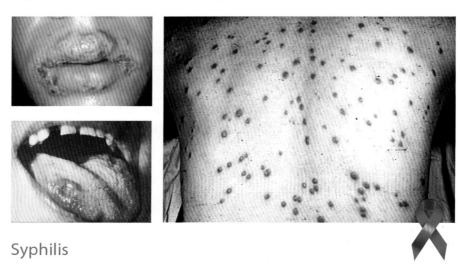

Syphilis

Syphilis is one of the most serious of the sexually-transmitted diseases, as it affects most parts of the body, even after many years. It is a serious disease, if left without treatment, may lead to bad results years after the initial infection, which make it more serious even though the initial symptoms may be simple and cause no alarm.

It causes chancres (painless lesions) which may disappear by themselves within two or three weeks, during which the disease may have spread to most parts of the body.

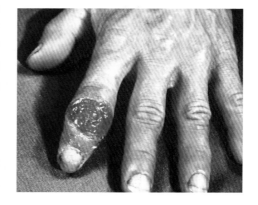

How it is spread

Syphilis spreads via direct sexual contact or kissing, or via transfusion of blood from a sick person to a healthy, unaffected one, or via nursing a carrier of the disease, or by using personal items or drinking water directly from a cup that he has used.

Symptoms of syphilis

There are three stages of this disease:

• The initial stage

The chancre or lesion of syphilis, which is a small ulcer that does not attract attention, like a cigarette burn. This chancre grows larger and then heals itself after about six weeks.

The incubation period of this disease is between three and six weeks, and this chancre may appear on the limbs and in places where there is friction.

• The secondary stage

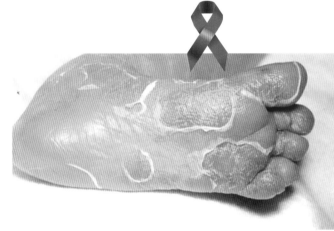

The syphilis bacteria spread throughout the body. This stage begins after the appearance of syphilis chancres, and may be delayed by several months. In this stage a severe skin rash appears in more than 80 percent of cases, and the patient develops infections in the bones, eye and liver, along with nausea and vomiting, constipation, muscular pain, elevated temperature, headache and overall weakness. After the skin symptoms disappear within a few weeks of the secondary stage, the disease enters a dormant phase where no symptoms appear.

Effected new born's foot

• The final stage

This stage is distinguished by the appearance of boils which spread throughout the body. This stage may least from three to seven years.

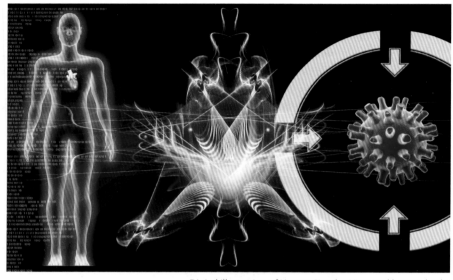

Digital illustration of Herpes Simplex Virus and human body

Herpes

Herpes is one of the most serious sexually-transmitted diseases because it spreads rapidly. It is spread by direct contact with the sick person and using his personal items, kissing, sitting on toilet seats, and proximity to the sick person. Hence, it is not limited to the West; it has spread via some travelers to and from the Middle East.

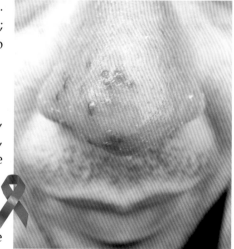

Site of infection

It affects the genitals, perineum, anus, upper thighs, scrotal sac, cervix, glans and shaft of the penis.

Symptoms

Herpes starts with the emergence of lesions on the genitals, and the patient may feel

A medical condition closeup of the common cold sore virus herpes simplex on an infected victims nose. Triggers can be viral or from strong sun exposure

general exhaustion and that he is in poor health. The patient is affected immediately after exposure, and the incubation period before the appearance of symptoms lasts for about five days. The sickness begins with small infected spots on the skin, where a number of small pus-filled lesions appear, forming bubbles surrounded by a red area. Then they burst and appear like wet scratches on the skin covered with a translucent substance.

AIDS

AIDS stands for Acquired Immune Deficiency Syndrome. It is an epidemic that has resulted from immorality. Professor Luc Montagnier is regarded as the first discoverer of the disease. More than 740 cases of the disease were discovered in 1985, according to statements of the World Health Organization. It is a disease for which there is no cure, and a slow death is inevitable. This disease, like other sexually-transmitted diseases, has an incubation period which varies from three to seven years. A person may be carrying the disease with no apparent symptoms.

Al-Hawadith magazine (issue No. 1526, 21 January 1986) published an interview with Dr. Mattfried Frankeh of Bonn, who specializes in

AIDS. We will quote some of his answers to the questions posed:

- **Question**: I have heard that AIDS may be transmitted by kissing. What is your view?

- **Answer**: Yes, that is correct, and it happens if the kiss is forceful with mixing of saliva, or if the kiss results in a small wound inside the mouth, because it is possible for the AIDS virus to enter the blood stream through wounds, no matter how small.

- **Question**: What are the symptoms of AIDS infection, and what happens inside the body?

- **Answer**: If a person is infected with AIDS, the incubation period may last anywhere from three to seven years. As for what happens inside the body, the virus enters the bloodstream, after which it becomes dangerous; it affects the immune cells, which are the white blood cells, as a result of

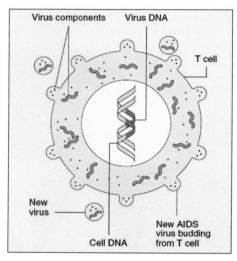

which the function of these cells is compromised, and the body's immunity begins to decline while the virus increases. When immunity is reduced, the body cannot resist any disease.

- **Question**: What is the story of AIDS? Where did it come from? How did it begin?

- **Answer**: The virus first appeared in the seventies in Central Africa, where this type of virus was carried by one type of monkey that was eaten by the inhabitants. It is possible that an American who went there as a tourist contracted the virus from one of the locals who was infected with AIDS, and this tourist brought the virus back with him to America, and because he was an active homosexual, the disease began to spread until it reached us.

Various other sexually-transmitted diseases

- Genital warts: This disease spreads via swimming pools and public baths, and may also be spread via touching and sexual contact. It appears as a white lesion with a waxy layer. It affects the genitals and anus, but the patient does not feel any pain unless infection occurs.

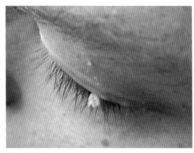

Genital warts

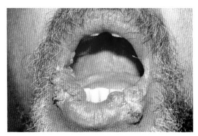

Genital warts

- Pubic lice which are transmitted via sexual contact and direct touching

Pubic lice

- Scabies. This affects all of the body except the face, and is transmitted via touching. It causes severe itching.

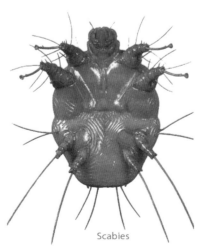

Scabies

There are other sexually transmitted diseases with varying incubation periods which may cause painful itching, boils and lesions in the genitals, anus and elsewhere.

Learning an important lesson

We should learn a lesson from this story:

A young man went to a Western country as a tourist, and he rented a furnished apartment. Ladies of the night started coming to him and he could not resist the overwhelming temptation. After indulging his basic instincts, he ended up in a pathetic state, because he now carried the germs that cause syphilis and gonorrhoea. A

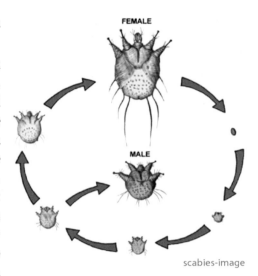

scabies-image

few years later he got married, and when his wife did not conceive children, he took her to a doctor and the doctor asked him for a sperm sample. The results showed that he was severely affected by the germs that he carried, so no treatment could help him. The doctor said to him, "This is Allah's punishment for you in this world, and if you do not repent and seek forgiveness, the punishment in the Hereafter will be even worse."

From Pretoria to Washington, chastity struggles to survive

As a result of the spread of immorality and corruption, statistics indicate that the number of rape cases in South Africa has reached alarming proportions. Research has shown that a woman is raped every thirty seconds in that country which has been liberated from apartheid long time ago. A journalist by the name of Charlene Smith reported that her turn came when a man carrying a butcher's knife broke into her house, tied her hands and raped her. After the rape, Smith had to cope with bureaucratic nurses and hospitals that are ill-equipped to treat rape victims with anti-AIDS drugs.

South Africa is regarded as one of the most crime-ridden countries in the world. For every 100,000 people there are 116 cases of rape, which is almost double the annual rate of murder, which in 1998 reached a

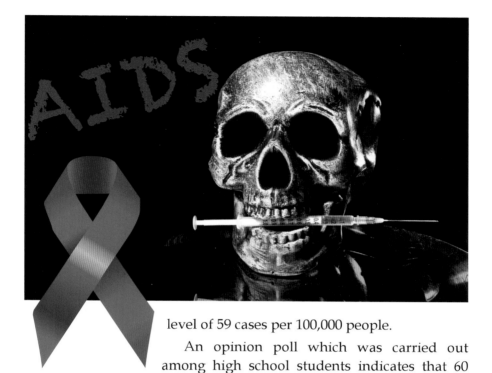

level of 59 cases per 100,000 people.

An opinion poll which was carried out among high school students indicates that 60 percent of girls are apprehensive of being raped before they graduate!

The security forces estimate the number of reported rape cases are no more than 9 percent of the total number of rapes that actually take place in South Africa, which raises the total number of women and girls who are raped every year to more than a million of the female inhabitants of the country.

A women's anti-rape group indicates that the police usually underestimate the real number of rape victims. For every case of rape that is reported, there are thirty-five other victims who keep quiet. One of the consequences of rape is the spread of AIDS, because one in every eight adults in South Africa is infected with HIV, and the rate of infection has spread to 1,500 per day.

Reports state that most victims of rape in South Africa are unable to afford anti-AIDS drugs which cost between 2,000 and 4,000 rand (330-660 dollars). These drugs are not sponsored by the government,

which has been subjected to severe criticism by opposition parties for its failure to prevent the crime of rape and its inability to tackle crime at its source and contain its effects quickly. The judicial system is heavily burdened and does not have the ability to deal with cases quickly, hospitals are poorly equipped and the country is dominated by a culture of apathy and silence and a failure to understand that rape is a serious crime.

On the other hand, a study in the United States carried out under the auspices of the Department of Health, Justice and Social Affairs has shown that nearly 18 percent of women (17.7 million women) in the United States have been raped or almost raped at some stage in their lives. It is worth mentioning that more than half of rape victims were below the age of 17 when they were raped for the first time.

The American Ministry of Social Affairs and Health commented on these figures, saying, "Every one of these figures represents our daughters, our mothers and our neighbors. We have to admit that violence against women (which is caused by free mixing and liberalism) has become a serious social problem."

From another angle, statistics compiled by the Center for Policy Studies, located in Denver, under the heading of National Violence Against Women, indicate that more than half of women have been exposed to physical aggression at various stages in their lives, from slaps on the face and punches to the use of firearms. The research included interviews with approximately 8,000 men and 8,000 women. Do we not have the right to say praise be to Allah Who has saved us from what many of His creation are suffering? So we should repeat the words of Allah, the Exalted:

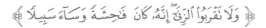

"And come not near to unlawful sex. Verily, it is a Fahishah (i.e. anything that transgresses its limits: a great sin, and an evil way that leads one to hell unless Allah Forgives him)." (Soorah Al-Isra, 17:32)

*****

Pork

The basic principle is that Muslims should obey Allah in whatever He commands, and refrain from whatever He forbids, whether the wisdom behind it is apparent or not. Allah, Most High, says:

﴾ وَمَا كَانَ لِمُؤْمِنٍ وَلَا مُؤْمِنَةٍ إِذَا قَضَى ٱللَّهُ وَرَسُولُهُۥ أَمْرًا أَن يَكُونَ لَهُمُ ٱلْخِيَرَةُ مِنْ أَمْرِهِمْ وَمَن يَعْصِ ٱللَّهَ وَرَسُولَهُۥ فَقَدْ ضَلَّ ضَلَٰلًا مُّبِينًا ﴿

"It is not for a Believer, man or woman, when Allah and His Messenger have decreed a matter that they should have any option in their decision. And whoever disobeys Allah and His Messenger, he has indeed strayed into a plain error." (Soorah Al-Ahzab, 33:36)

Concerning the wisdom behind the prohibition on pork, Dr. 'Abd Al-Fattah Idrees, professor of comparative *Fiqh* in the University of Al-Azhar, says, that Islam forbids eating pork and there is a great deal of evidence concerning that, such as the words of Allah:

$$ ﴿ قُل لَّآ أَجِدُ فِي مَآ أُوحِيَ إِلَيَّ مُحَرَّمًا عَلَىٰ طَاعِمٍ يَطْعَمُهُۥ إِلَّآ أَن يَكُونَ مَيْتَةً $$

$$ أَوْ دَمًا مَّسْفُوحًا أَوْ لَحْمَ خِنزِيرٍ فَإِنَّهُۥ رِجْسٌ أَوْ فِسْقًا أُهِلَّ لِغَيْرِ ٱللَّهِ بِهِۦ ۚ $$

$$ فَمَنِ ٱضْطُرَّ غَيْرَ بَاغٍ وَلَا عَادٍ فَإِنَّ رَبَّكَ غَفُورٌ رَّحِيمٌ ﴾ $$

"Say (O Muhammad): I find not in that which has been revealed to me anything forbidden to be eaten by one who wishes to eat it, unless it be Maitah (a dead animal) or blood poured forth (by slaughtering or the like), or the flesh of swine (pork); for that surely is impure or impious (unlawful) meat (of an animal) which is slaughtered as a sacrifice for others than Allah (or has been slaughtered for idols, or on which Allah's Name has not been mentioned while slaughtering)..." (Soorah Al-An'am, 6:145)

$$ ﴿ حُرِّمَتْ عَلَيْكُمُ ٱلْمَيْتَةُ وَٱلدَّمُ وَلَحْمُ ٱلْخِنزِيرِ وَمَآ أُهِلَّ لِغَيْرِ ٱللَّهِ بِهِۦ ﴾ $$

"Forbidden to you (for food) are (the dead animals, beast not slaughtered), blood, the flesh of swine, and that on which Allah's Name has not been mentioned while slaughtering (that which has been slaughtered as a sacrifice for others than Allah, or has been slaughtered for idols)..." (Soorah Al-Ma'idah, 5:3).

The apparent meaning of these two Verses indicates that it is *Haram* to eat the flesh of pigs, but the scholars have stated that it is *Haram* to eat all parts of the pig, even if it is not actually the meat, and they explained that the reason why the flesh is singled out for mention in the two Verses, and not other parts, is that the flesh is what is usually sought from pigs. Hence, Imam An-Nawawi and Imam Ibn Qudamah, may Allah have Mercy upon them, narrated that there was consensus among the Muslims on the prohibition on eating any part of the pig. Ibn Hazm, may Allah have Mercy upon him, said that the scholars are unanimously agreed that it is *Haram*, so it is not permissible to eat anything from it, whether it is the flesh, fat, sinews, gristle, stomach, brain, trotters or anything else.

Even though the Lawgiver has stated the reason for the prohibition on eating it, which is that it is "impure" and the Muslims must avoid it, it is not only for that reason; rather it has been forbidden because it is evil and contains many harmful things which could lead to the death of the one who eats it. Scientific and medical research has proved that the pig, unlike other animals, is regarded as the greatest storehouse of germs that are harmful to the human body. Among the diseases that may result from eating its meat are the following:

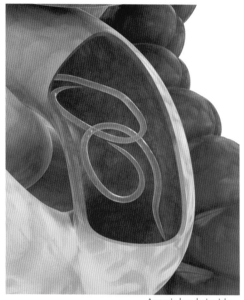

Ascaris lumbricoides

- Parasitic diseases, such as that caused by roundworm, which is the most dangerous parasitic worms for humans. Pork is not free of these worms, which gather in the muscles of the one who eats pork containing the worms, causing him severe pain and making him unable to move these muscles. They also collect in the diaphragm in large numbers causing him to stop breathing and then die.

Another worm is the tapeworm which may reach a length of ten feet. It can cause digestive problems and anaemia, let alone vesicles in the brain, liver, lungs and spinal cord of the one who eats pork, along with other problems.

Doctors confirm that tapeworm disease is regarded as one of the serious diseases that result from eating pork. The worm develops in the small intestine and matures within a few months into an adult worm, with a body composed of a thousand segments and a length between 4 and 10 meters. It lives alone in the human intestine, and its eggs are excreted with the faeces.

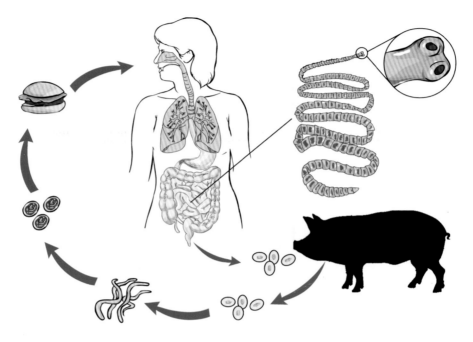

When the pig swallows and digests the egg, it enters the tissues and muscles and forms a sac containing fluid and the head of the tapeworm.

The *Ascaris* worm causes a lung infection and blockage in the intestines and elsewhere.

And there are many other parasites which cause harm in various parts of the body of the one who eats pork.

- Bacterial disease such as tuberculosis, cholera, typhoid, paratyphoid, Maltese fever and so on.
- Viral diseases such as encephalitis, myocarditis, influenza, stomatitis and so on
- Protozoan diseases such as *Toxoplasma gondii* which causes fever, exhaustion, enlargement of the liver and spleen, pneumonitis, myocarditis and meningitis in addition to loss of hearing and vision
- Diseases resulting from the biological structure of the flesh and fat of the pig, due to the high level of uric acid in the blood,

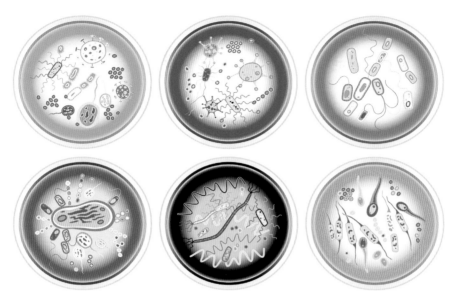

Six Petri Dishes with Bacterial Colonies of Different Colors

because the pig excretes only 2 percent of this acid, and the remainder becomes part of the pig's flesh.

Hence, those who eat pork suffer from joint pain. In addition to that, its flesh contains saturated fat, unlike the fat of other animals. Those who eat pork accumulate greater levels of fat in their bodies and the level of cholesterol in their blood is elevated, which makes them susceptible to arteriosclerosis, heart disease and angina pectoris which may lead to sudden death.

This is in addition to the indigestion suffered by pork eaters, as this meat remains in the stomach for nearly four hours until it is fully digested, unlike other kinds of meat. Eating pork also leads to obesity and fills the body of those who eat it with vesicles, pustules and fatty deposits,.

These harmful effects and others indicate that the wise Lawgiver only forbade pork for a great reason,

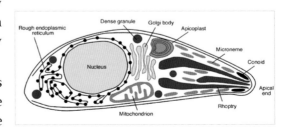

Toxo_ultrastructure

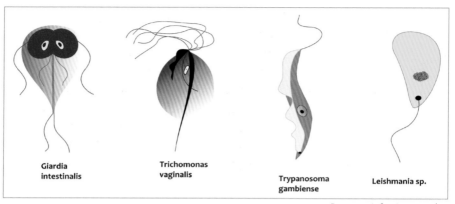

Giardia intestinalis

Trichomonas vaginalis

Trypanosoma gambiense

Leishmania sp.

Protozoa infecting people

namely the preservation of life, which is one of the five necessities in *Shari'ah*. And Allah knows best.

There is also a general explanation which includes pork and other forbidden foods. Allah, the Exalted, says:

﴿ وَيُحَرِّمُ عَلَيْهِمُ ٱلْخَبَٰٓئِثَ ﴾

"And prohibits them as unlawful Al-Khaba'ith (i.e. all evil and unlawful as regards things, deeds, beliefs, persons and foods)." (Soorah Al-A'raf 7:157)

Everything that Allah, the Almighty, has forbidden is *Khabeeth* (evil), and in this context, *Al-Khaba'ith* (evil things) includes everything that spoils man's life in terms of his health, wealth and morals.

The Muslims in earlier times did not know the details of the harms or the extent of the unhygienic nature

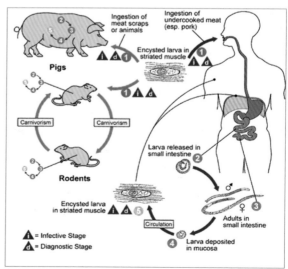

Trichinella_LifeCycle

of pork, or the reason why it was forbidden, until modern discoveries showed that pork contains disease-causing factors and harmful germs that were previously unknown, such as the fact that the pork that man consumes contains worms that are hazardous to human health and that grow in the human intestine in a way that cannot be treated with medicine to expel them; rather they grow inside human muscles in a way that medicine even today cannot treat to rid humanity of them, and they pose a danger to man's life. This worm is called the *Trichina* worm. Hence, the wisdom behind Islam's prohibition on pork is quite clear.

The French *Larousse* encyclopaedia says that this worm (*Trichina*) is transmitted to man and heads for the heart, where it settles in the muscles, especially in the chest, side, larynx, eye and diaphragm, and the embryos remain active in the body for many years. But we cannot think

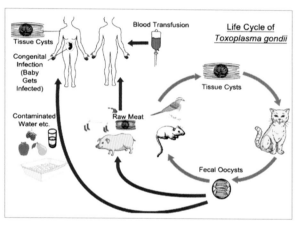

toxoplasma-gondii-life-cycle

that this discovery is the only reason why pork is forbidden; rather science, which discovered these problems in pork, could in the future discover other problems that are not yet known.

Therefore, from the Islamic viewpoint, the opinion of those who say that raising pigs using modern methods and technology to supervise its feeding, sleeping and living guarantees that it will be free of these germs, is unacceptable.

If we understand that the Islamic texts which forbid pork are general in meaning and not connected to any reason, then it is possible that there may be other harmful effects in pork other than those that have been discovered, as science is always progressing.

It should also be noted that although it may be possible to raise

pigs using technology to avoid these problems at some times or in some places where civilization is advanced, it is not possible to do that everywhere on earth. The rulings of *Shari'ah* have to be suitable and applicable for all people in all places; hence, the prohibition is general and inclusive. And Allah knows best.

(Fatwa Center supervised by Dr. 'Abdullah Al-Faqeeh)

I say: In addition to what have been explained above about the disease which it causes to the one who eats it, there is another, more serious disease, which is the disease of cuckoldry and lack of protective jealousy. Modern medical science says that eating pork may be one of the causes of the loss of protective jealousy among Europeans and the emergence of various kinds of sexual perversion such as wife-swapping and plural marriage. It is well-known that even if pigs are raised in clean pens, if they are left to live freely in the forest they will revert to their original nature and eat dead bodies that they come across, and indeed they enjoy that more than the vegetables and potatoes that they were used to eating in the clean, sterilized pens. (See: *Tahreem Lahm Al-Jawarih*)

*****

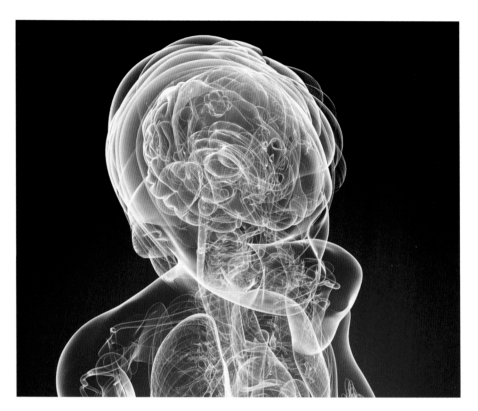

Worm in a Woman's Brain After a Meal of Pork

American doctors extracted a parasitic worm from a woman's brain after a period of health problems which affected her after she ate a famous Mexican dish containing pork.

The American woman said that she felt very sick for three weeks after eating the pork dish, and that the doctors in the Mayo Clinic Hospital in Arizona kept her in hospital on 14/4/2001 after they discovered vesicles in her brain resulting from the presence of a parasitic worm. They told her that she needed surgery urgently.

Doctors confirmed that the particular pork dish that the American woman had eaten in Mexico must have contained the lethal parasitic

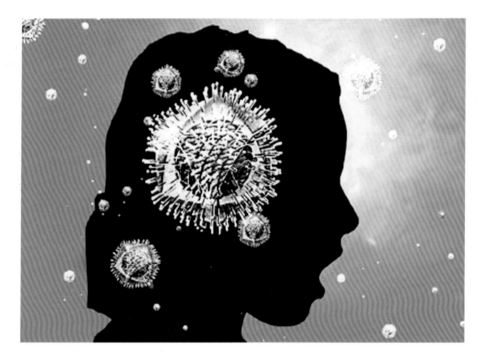

intestinal worm known by the Latin name of *Taenas solium* (pork tapeworm). This is a parasitic worm that is transmitted to humans by eating undercooked meat.

Dr. Joseph Serfin explained that the egg of the worm had attached itself to the woman's stomach wall at first and then it had moved through the bloodstream until it finally reached her brain. When the worm reached the brain, it caused very little damage at first, but when it died and finally began to disintegrate, it caused a severe tissue infection in the surrounding area.

The woman, Dawn Basera, said, "The idea of having a worm in my brain felt very weird. Suddenly, I realized that they were going to open up my brain and take a worm out from it, and this was a dreadful shock."

Of course, this woman went ahead with this operation, which lasted for six hours, to remove the worm from her head. The surgery was done using a local anaesthetic, because she had to be awake and conscious during the surgery, which was done on a very sensitive area of the brain, and they had to talk to her during the surgery so that none of the sensitive areas would be affected.

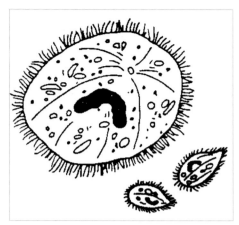

Finally, the doctors found the rotten worm and removed it without causing any long-term damage. Dr. Sefin, who supervised the procedure, said, "She was extremely lucky, because we only found one abscess in her brain."

lethal parasitic intestinal worm

Basera recovered quickly, but doctors told her that she needs regular check-ups for six months, and the incident is still causing some health problems.

I say: This happened even though she ate a meal of pork that was supervised by the health department – or so they claim – and that was raised on specialized farms far from the dirt and filth that pigs usually eat.

Is there any proof after that for those so-called Muslims who defend pork, after seeing the physical harm that results from it and that could take away life altogether, as happened in the case of the woman mentioned above?

*****

Islamic Prohibition on Tattoos

A tattoo is a permanent drawing or a mark made on a person's skin. It is usually done on areas that remain uncovered, especially on the face, legs and arms. It is done using colored substances and tools that pierce the skin. The primary aim of tattoos is to attract the attention of others and reduce differences between people, and it is used for cosmetic purposes. It may also be connected to myths and false beliefs about means of protection against evil. The ancient Egyptians believed that tattoos could heal sickness, and that they warded off the evil eye and destructive envy. Tattoos are also regarded as a kind of mortification of the flesh, and there was a tradition in ancient times of mortifying the flesh for deities or for the priests or sorcerers who represented the gods or deities, i.e., in certain circumstances or on certain occasions, a youth or man would be required to subject his body to scarification or branding as a kind of sacrifice, so that the scars would bring him protection or strength or good luck.

It may be noted that 5-9 percent of Christians and Muslims get tattoos, although it is forbidden in both religions. Islam curses the one who does it, and in Christianity it has been forbidden since the Council of Nicea, and was forbidden altogether by the seventh religious council because it was regarded as an idolatrous custom. Women took a particular interest in this art until it became almost synonymous with them, as they did it for cosmetic purposes. Men did not merely look at women's adornments, however; they eventually tried it for themselves. Among the male groups who are particularly known for that are soldiers, prisoners and sailors.

Tattooing is done in two ways. One uses tools such as needles and sharp knives to pierce the skin and make wounds in it. The other method uses colored substances derived from animals or other powders such as kohl, coal and plant juices.

Many countries realized the harm that it causes, and banned it. In 1969, Martin Madoun introduced legislation to ban tattoos officially in England, and the Japanese government in 1870 issued a law forbidding tattoos.

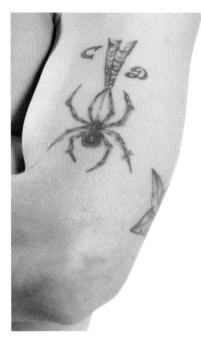

In a report published on aljazeera.net, quoting from the Reuters news agency on Friday 17/7/2003, the European Council warned that tattoo hobbyists were injecting their skin with a poisonous chemical substance, due to prevalent ignorance of the materials used in dyeing the skin. It said that most of the chemicals used in tattooing are artificial dyes that were originally made for other purposes such as car paint or printers' inks, and there are no statements to prove that they are safe for use in tattooing, or such proof is rare. In a statement accompanying the report on the health dangers of tattooing and body piercing, the committee asked: Would you like your skin to be injected with car paint?

The report said: In addition to the danger of infection with disease such as the HIV virus which causes AIDS, or hepatitis or bacterial infections resulting from contaminated needles, tattooing may also cause skin cancer, psoriasis and shock resulting from severe infection caused by poisoning or even changes in behavior.

More than fourteen hundred years ago, the Prophet, peace and blessings of Allah be upon him, forbade tattooing and cursed the one

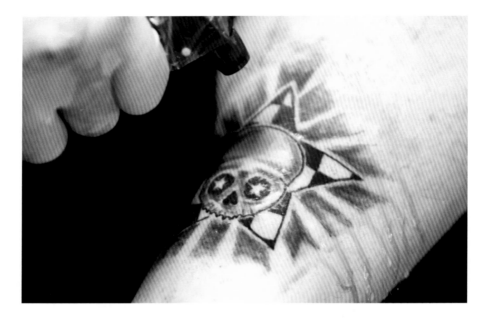

who does it. "Curse" means being expelled from the mercy of Allah, which indicates that this *Shari'ah* was indeed revealed by One Who is Kind and All-Knowing.

It was narrated from Abu Juhaifah, may Allah be pleased with him: "That the Messenger of Allah, peace and blessings of Allah be upon him, forbade the price of blood, the price of a dog, the earnings of a slave woman (who is forced into prostitution), and he cursed the woman who does tattoos and the woman who has them done, the one who consumes *Riba* (interest) and the one who pays it, and he cursed the one who makes images." (Narrated by Al-Bukhari)

It was narrated from Abu Hurairah, may Allah be pleased with him, that the Prophet, peace and blessings of Allah be upon him, said: "May Allah curse the woman who does hair extensions and the woman who has that done, and the woman who does tattoos and the woman who has them done." (Agreed upon)

(*Al-Shabakah Al-Islamiyah*, an article by Sheikh 'Abd As-Salam Al-Basyooni on tattoos)

* * * * *

Chapter:12

Prohibition of Blood

Allah, the Exalted, says in His Book:

قُل لَّآ أَجِدُ فِي مَآ أُوحِيَ إِلَيَّ مُحَرَّمًا عَلَىٰ طَاعِمٍ يَطْعَمُهُۥ إِلَّآ أَن يَكُونَ مَيْتَةً أَوْ دَمًا مَّسْفُوحًا أَوْ لَحْمَ خِنزِيرٍ فَإِنَّهُۥ رِجْسٌ أَوْ فِسْقًا أُهِلَّ لِغَيْرِ ٱللَّهِ بِهِۦ فَمَنِ ٱضْطُرَّ غَيْرَ بَاغٍ وَلَا عَادٍ فَإِنَّ رَبَّكَ غَفُورٌ رَّحِيمٌ

"Say (O Muhammad): 'I find not in that which has been revealed to me anything forbidden to be eaten by the one who wishes to eat it, unless it be Maitah (a dead animal) or blood poured forth (by slaughtering or the like), or the flesh of swine (pork); for that surely, is impure or impious (unlawful) meat (of an animal) which is slaughtered as a sacrifice for others than Allah (or has been slaughtered for idols, or on which Allah's Name has not been mentioned while slaughtering). But whosoever is forced by necessity without wilful disobedience, nor transgressing due limits; (for him) certainly, your Lord is Oft-Forgiving, Most Merciful.'" (Soorah Al-An'am, 6:145)

And the Qur'an described the Prophet, peace and blessings of Allah be upon him, in the following terms:

﴿وَيُحِلُّ لَهُمُ الطَّيِّبَتِ وَيُحَرِّمُ عَلَيْهِمُ الْخَبَّئِثَ﴾

"He allows them as lawful At-Tayyibat (i.e. all good and lawful as regards things, deeds, beliefs, persons and foods), and prohibits them as unlawful Al-Khaba'ith (i.e. all evil and unlawful as regards things, deeds, beliefs, persons and foods)." (Soorah Al-A'raf, 7:157)

Science has proved beyond any shadow of a doubt that blood, which Allah, the Exalted, has created in the flesh of animals, carries many harmful germs. Hence, we can understand the wisdom and aim of *Shari'ah* in the method of slaughter enjoined by the Lawgiver before meat can be eaten, because this method of slaughter expels the harmful, unclean blood.

The reason why blood is forbidden is what modern science has proved, that blood is regarded as an ideal environment for germs to multiply and grow; moreover it contains nothing of nutritional value and is very difficult to digest; if any of it enters the human stomach, the person will vomit straightaway, or it will be expelled in the faeces without having been digested, appearing as a black substance.

All scientific research concerning this matter has confirmed that the harm resulting from drinking blood or cooking it is very grave indeed, because of the germs that blood contains, let alone the fact that blood – contrary to what is imagined – is very poor in nutritional content and the amount of protein it contains is mixed with highly toxic and harmful elements, which makes eating it a very risky venture which exposes one to danger. It also contains poisonous

elements, foremost among which is carbon dioxide, which is a lethal gas. This also explains the prohibition on eating meat of animals that have been strangled,

"That which has been killed by strangling," (Soorah Al-Ma'idah, 5:3)

because it only dies from a buildup of this gas in its blood, which leads to its death.

What we have mentioned of the bad consequences that result from consuming blood is sufficient, we think, for it to be prohibited and for laws to be introduced forbidding that.

It remains for us to say that Islam may pardon a small amount of blood because it is not possible to avoid it, and a small amount does not cause harm. Hence, the Qur'anic text forbids blood that is actually shed:

﴾أَوۡ دَمًا مَّسۡفُوحًا﴿

"Blood poured forth." (Soorah Al-An'am, 6:145).

This indicates that blood, which remains in the meat, is not included in the prohibition. Al-Tabari, may Allah have Mercy upon him, says

concerning that, Allah stipulated, when He forbade blood to His slaves, that it is only the blood that is poured forth that is forbidden; the conclusion is clear that if it is not shed or poured forth, then it is *Halal* and is not *Najis* (impure).

Glory be to the One Who taught His Prophet, peace and blessings of Allah be upon him, which which he did not know, and blessed him thereby, as He said:

﴿ وَعَلَّمَكَ مَا لَمْ تَكُن تَعْلَمُ وَكَانَ فَضْلُ اللَّهِ عَلَيْكَ عَظِيمًا ﴾

"And taught you that which you knew not. And Ever Great is the Grace of Allah unto you (O Muhammad)." (Soorah An-Nisa', 4:113).

Glory be to the One Who honored the world with this great religion and straight path:

﴿ قَدْ جَاءَكُمْ رَسُولُنَا يُبَيِّنُ لَكُمْ كَثِيرًا مِّمَّا كُنتُمْ تُخْفُونَ مِنَ الْكِتَابِ وَيَعْفُوا عَن كَثِيرٍ قَدْ جَاءَكُم مِّنَ اللَّهِ نُورٌ وَكِتَابٌ مُّبِينٌ ﴾

"Now has come to you Our Messenger (Muhammad صلى الله عليه وسلم) explaining to you much of that which you used to hide from the Scripture and pass over (i.e. leaving out without explaining) much. Indeed, there has come to you from Allah a light (Prophet Muhammad) and a plain Book (this Qur>an)." (Soorah Al-Ma'idah, 5:15).

He indeed spoke the truth who said: "*Blood is the place where disease breeds.*"

* * * * *

In the Islamic way of slaughtering animals, the drain of whole blood is necessary.

The Wisdom Behind Halal Slaughter (*Dhabeehah*)

Halal slaughter is a specific manner of slaughtering, by means of which blood is expelled from the animal's body. That can only be done by cutting the main vein without cutting the head off, so that the connection between heart and brain remains and the heart beat continues to push the blood from the body. When the connection between brain and heart remains, the heart continues to beat, and thus the blood is expelled from the body and the slaughtered meat thus becomes pure, lest the cause of its death be violent shocks that it received in one of its faculties such as the brain, heart or liver. By cutting the main large vein, the blood is all drained from the body of the animal, because the heart beats until all the blood has been shed. This is the best method for slaughtering animals.

But if it is slaughtered by any other method, the blood remains in the veins and in all parts of the animal and thus contaminates all the meat; because of the presence of uric acid in the blood and the presence of the blood in the meat, all of that is absorbed by man when he eats the meat. Hence, the person who eats meat slaughtered by non-Islamic methods suffers more from infections and joint pains, because this

uric acid accumulates in the joints. Purification of the meat is done by draining out the blood. When our Lord forbade blood to us, it was because of the presence of this poisonous substance, namely uric acid.

It is obvious that everything that Allah, the Almighty, has forbidden to us was only forbidden because of His knowledge and because He created us and He knows best what is beneficial for us. The one who goes against the command of Allah must bear its consequences.

It is worth mentioning that we are to remember Allah, the Exalted, when slaughtering. The Prophet, peace and blessings of Allah be upon him, taught us that. Saying *Bismillah* (in the Name of Allah) and *Allahu Akbar* (Allah is Greatest) are among the *Sunnah* practices to be followed when slaughtering meat.

Another *Sunnah* of the Prophet, peace and blessings of Allah be upon him, is to make the blood flow strongly by cutting the jugular vein, because it is essential to drain out this blood, that carries all the elements of disease, from the animal. Scientists say that the animal which retains blood in its veins is harmful; it produces acids which lead to the meat becoming dry and hard. After three hours the aerobic and anaerobic germs will have the opportunity to spoil this fleshy tissue in which the blood remains. This process produces foul-smelling substances and toxic effects and the flesh swells up due to the gases that are produced.

Hence, the Prophet, peace and blessings of Allah be upon him, taught us that it is essential to slaughter meat by cutting the jugular veins, so that the blood will be drained out from its body and the meat will remain pure and good.

This is the wisdom of our Lord, Who forbade us (in *Soorah Al-Ma'idah* 5:3) to eat that which has been killed by strangulation, or by a violent blow (by beating with a rod or rock), or after a headlong fall from a high place, or by being gored by another animal and that which has been (partly) eaten by a wild animal (unless it is still alive and can be slaughtered in the proper manner) and so on. In all these cases,

the blood remains in the animal's body, and the blood contains all the factors that cause disease and spoiling, hardening and swelling of the meat. So it is essential that the meat be slaughtered in the prescribed manner.

But the Prophet, peace and blessings of Allah be upon him, exempted fish from this condition that its blood be drained out. One may wonder why is it that fish may be eaten if they die in a way other than *Halal*

method of slaughter. Is the blood of fish different from the blood of other creatures?

The scientists answer this question by noting that fish have a special characteristic that Allah, the Exalted, has created in them. When the fish is caught and taken out of the water and dies, all its blood collects in its epiglottis. When the epiglottis turns red, it means that all the blood has come to it. Hence, the Prophet, peace and blessings of Allah be upon him, made an exception for fish, which unlike other animals may be eaten although they die without *Halal* method of slaughter. This is a sign of his Prophethood and that he did not speak on the basis of his own whims and desires. When he enjoined these guidelines it was because they contained subtle wisdom that science only discovered slowly.

Al-'Ijaz Al-'Ilmi by Dr. An-Nabulsi

*****

Prohibition on the Meat of Carnivores

It was narrated that Ibn 'Abbas, may Allah be pleased with him, said: "The Messenger of Allah, peace and blessings of Allah be upon him, forbade every animal that has fangs and every bird that has talons." (Narrated by Muslim)

Modern nutritional science has proved that people acquire some of the characteristics of the animals they eat, because their flesh contains some toxins and internal secretions that flow in the blood and may be transferred to people's stomachs, thus affecting their characteristics.

It has become clear that when predators are about to pounce on their prey, their bodies secrete hormones and substances that help them to fight and catch their prey. Dr. C. Lepage, a professor of nutritional science in Britain, says: These secretions appear in the animal even when it is kept in a cage, when it is given a piece of meat to eat. He explains

this theory of his by saying, "All you have to do is visit the zoo once and look at the agitated movements of the tiger when it is biting and chewing a piece of meat; see the look of anger and the frown on its face. Then look at the elephant and see how calm and peaceful it looks when it is eating and when it is playing with children and visitors. Look at the lion and compare its fierceness and viciousness with the calm and peaceful nature of the camel. It has been noticed that people who eat the flesh of carnivores or other animals whose meat is forbidden by Islam have a kind of viciousness and an inclination toward violence with no reason other than the desire to shed blood."

Studies and research have confirmed this phenomenon among various tribes which enjoy eating these kinds of meat, to the point that some of them may become so vicious that they eat human flesh.

These studies and researches have also proved another phenomenon among these tribes, which is that they also experience a kind of sexual chaos and lack of protectiveness concerning the opposite sex, let alone any kind of respect for the family system and issues of honor.

Their state is closer to that of predatory animals, where one male will attack and kill another so that he can take the females, until another male comes along who is younger and stronger, and he kills the first usurper and so on.

In the *American Encyclopaedia* it says: Every hundred pounds of pork contains fifty pounds of fat, i.e. a ratio of 50 percent, whereas lamb contains approximately 17 percent of fat and veal contains no more than 5 percent. Tests have proved that pork fat (lard) contains a large amount of complex fatty acids. The level of cholesterol in pork is more than ten times the level in beef. This fact has serious implications because these fats increase the cholesterol levels in a person's blood, and when this substance increases beyond the natural average, it accumulates in the arteries, especially in the arteries of the heart. Then it causes hardening of the arteries and a rise in blood pressure, which is the main cause of most cases of angina pectoris, which is common in Europe. It is clear from statistics that have been published about angina and hardening of the arteries that the rate of these diseases in Europe is five times greater than in the Muslim world. This is in addition to the effects of nervous tension which cannot be denied. It is also worth mentioning that those animals which eat meat have fangs, as referred to in the narration under discussion, because they have four large fangs, two each in the upper and lower jaws.

This is not limited to animals only, rather it includes birds too; they may be divided into plant-eaters such as chickens and pigeons, and meat-eaters such as eagles and falcons. The scientific difference between them is as follows:

Birds that eat meat have sharp claws, which are not found in tame and domesticated birds. It is well-known that human nature is naturally put off from eating the flesh of animals and birds that eat meat, except in some societies which may be said to be uncivilized or some backward tribes, as we have indicated above. It is an amazing truth that Islam defined these scientific categories and pointed them out more than fourteen hundred years ago.

Al-'Ijaz Al-'Ilmi Fil-Islam Wal-Sunnah An-Nabawiyah

* * * * *

Prohibition on Intercourse With Women During Their Menses

Allah, the Exalted, says:

﴿ وَيَسْـَٔلُونَكَ عَنِ ٱلْمَحِيضِ قُلْ هُوَ أَذًى فَٱعْتَزِلُوا۟ ٱلنِّسَآءَ فِى ٱلْمَحِيضِ وَلَا تَقْرَبُوهُنَّ حَتَّىٰ يَطْهُرْنَ فَإِذَا تَطَهَّرْنَ فَأْتُوهُنَّ مِنْ حَيْثُ أَمَرَكُمُ ٱللَّهُ إِنَّ ٱللَّهَ يُحِبُّ ٱلتَّوَّٰبِينَ وَيُحِبُّ ٱلْمُتَطَهِّرِينَ ﴾

"They ask you concerning menstruation. Say: that is an Adha (a harmful thing for a husband to have a sexual intercourse with his wife while she is having her menses), therefore, keep away from women during menses and go not unto them till they are purified (from menses and have taken a bath). And when they have purified themselves, then go in unto them as Allah has ordained for you (go in unto them in any manner as long as it is in their vagina). Truly, Allah loves those who turn unto Him in repentance and loves those who purify themselves (by taking a bath and cleaning and washing thoroughly their private parts and bodies for their prayers)." (Soorah Al-Baqarah 2:222)

The scholars are unanimously agreed that the *Shari'ah* of Islam is based on what is in people's best interests in this world and the Hereafter. It is all justice and mercy and in people's best interests, as Ibn Al-Qayyim, may Allah have mercy on him, said.

Based on what the scholars are agreed upon, every ruling of *Shari'ah* must either bring some benefit or ward off some harm, and there must be wisdom behind it, whether it is apparent or not, whether some know it or some are ignorant of it.

Once this is established, the prohibition on intercourse with women during their menses comes under this heading. We may add to what has been noted above the facts that modern science has discovered in this area.

The Qur'anic text about menstruation mentions two things:

- It describes menstruation as *Adha* (a hurt and a pollution – Yusuf Ali)

- It enjoins keeping away from women during the menstrual period.

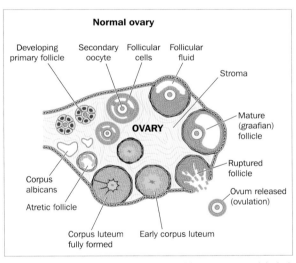

Diagramatic representation of normal human ovary -- labeled

With regard to the first matter, menstruation is natural blood that usually comes to adult women once every month, and the bleeding lasts for a period that varies between two and seven days in most cases. The amount of blood that comes out varies from one woman to another according to her physical and psychological state.

The flow of menstrual blood is due to important changes in the lining of the womb, which in turn leads to a rupture in blood vessels, thus causing a flow of blood; the lining of the womb falls away accompanied by bleeding, forming the menstrual flow.

The sanitary napkin lying on a red calendar

But the most serious impact of menses is the psychological and physical changes that affect the woman. Just before the menstruation period begins, the woman's red blood cell count falls, as well as an increase in symptoms of depression, trembling, nervous tension, mood swings and short temper. All of that may be accompanied by a change in the ability to judge things.

In addition to the changes mentioned above that happen to a woman during her menses, studies indicate that a woman's productivity decreases during her period, and there is a noticeable increase in women's suicide and crime rate during menses in some societies.

Based on the scientifically-proved changes that happen to women just before and during menses, we can understand the miraculous nature of the Qur'anic Verse which summed up all of that in just one word, *Adha*, as Allah, the Exalted, says:

﴿ قُلْ هُوَ أَذًى ﴾

"Say: that is an Adha (a hurt and a pollution)."

It may also be said that everyone to whom Allah, the Almighty, has granted a measure of sensitivity and humanity can clearly understand that the desire to have intercourse with a woman at the time of her menses is a bestial and unnatural desire; rather it is even lower and viler than that, because male animals choose the suitable time by instinct to approach the females. It is also known that intercourse during the woman's period cannot result in pregnancy at all, because ovulation can only happen two whole weeks before menses.

Moreover intercourse at the time of menses is in fact introducing germs into the uterus at a time when the woman's immune system is weak and vulnerable, and is unable to resist infection as required. It may be said that if Allah wills that they should have a child, then it will undoubtedly be born deformed, mentally deficient or unsound.

If we add to the above the fact that the presence of blood during this time is regarded as a factor that facilitates the multiplication and growth of germs, we can understand the miraculous nature of the Qur'anic prohibition on intercourse with women during menses.

From the above it is clear that intercourse with women during menses is not only contrary to what has been prescribed by Allah, the All-Knowing, and it is not only contrary to what is implied by fundamental good taste and pure nature, but it is also regarded as indulging in filth that is extremely harmful to the woman both physically and psychologically, and is regarded as sinking into the most primitive ignorance, especially after science has given its neutral verdict on this matter.

*****

Chapter:16

SMOKING

By Sheikh Muhammad Al-Mukhtar Al-Sulami

Mufti of the Tunisian Republic

Allah, the Exalted, says:

"He allows them as lawful At-Taiyyibat (i.e. all good and lawful as regards things, deeds, beliefs, persons and foods), and prohibits them as unlawful Al-Khaba'ith (i.e. all evil and unlawful as regards things, deeds, beliefs, persons and foods)." (Soorah Al-A'raf, 7:157).

The tobacco plant originated in America, so it was unknown to the old world until the discoverers of the American Continent brought it to Portugal and Spain, where it was cultivated and began to spread throughout Europe, North Africa, Turkey and elsewhere. People consume it in the form of powder (snuff) or smoke after burning it. It is consumed in the form of cigarettes, the smoke of which is inhaled by the user. The number of cigarettes manufactured in the latter half of the twentieth century runs into thousands of billions.

I say: In the texts of the jurists (*Fuqaha'*) before the tenth century A.H. we find no ruling on smoking, of course, but as soon as this habit spread, the Muslims turned to their jurists, who researched the matter and sought to come up with a ruling on it. Their views are as follows:

- That smoking is *Haram*, and they wrote essays and research supporting this view, which is held by the majority.

- That smoking is permissible. This is a view held by an extremely small minority.

- That smoking is *Makrooh* (disliked).

- That the ruling depends on the source of the tobacco, and the place and manner in which it is smoked. If it is produced in a Muslim country and not mixed with any *Haram* substance and is not consumed in a dubious or *Haram* gathering, and does not affect the person's dignity or cause him physical harm, then it is permissible, but if it fails to meet any of these conditions then it is *Haram*.

The ruling on whether something is *Halal* or *Haram* is not based on human authority, regardless of what that authority is; rather it is the ruling of Allah, the Almighty, according to which the doer will deserve either reward or punishment on the Day of Resurrection. Therefore, the ruling should be based on a text of Revelation or an analogy to something in a text or an application of a principle in *Shari'ah*. By paying attention to this principle we may discuss the ruling on tobacco in the following context:

Question: What if a person smokes tobacco on his own, or in a gathering with other smokers like him?

Answer: It seems most likely to me that if he will not be harmed by it, such as the one who has asthma or tuberculosis, or is pregnant, then smoking is very *Makrooh*, otherwise it is *Haram*.

Question: What is the ruling on smoking in the presence of non-smokers?

Answer: Because smoking penetrates the lungs of those who are present and may harm them, smoking is a transgression against them and is *Haram*.

Question: What is the ruling on cultivating tobacco, producing it, transporting it, selling it and acting as an agent to sell it?

Answer: It is very *Makrooh* and some of them said it is *Haram*.

Question: What is the ruling on advertising it and promoting it among people?

Answer: It is *Haram* because it is deceiving, cheating and concealing its negative aspects.

There may be three reasons why the harmful effects of smoking are covered up:

1. The large number of people who benefit from tobacco, starting with the growers until it reaches the hands of smokers, and the economic activity that accompanies all that, even among the countries that produce it. The economy has a great impact on decision-making.

2. The effect of the media which is used by tobacco companies to influence people's tastes, choices and standards. Decision-makers in the government should impose restrictions on the "media", to curb its role which destroys values and negatively influences people's reason, attitude, religious commitment and social standards. This is not a call to suppress freedom; rather it is a call to release freedom from those who want to strangle it in the name of freedom. Responsible freedom is that by virtue of which man is the *khalifah* of Allah, the Exalted, on Earth.

3. The budget of many countries is based on the income generated by tobacco, which is one of the things that countries turn to in order to make up shortfalls in the budget, by raising taxes on it. These are taxes that do not meet with any objection from the public, and they achieve the objective of collecting the estimated income because of the addiction factor and people's unwillingness to give it up.

I call upon governments to strike a balance between the losses that result from tobacco due to expenditure on public health, and the income that it generates. Undoubtedly they will realize that smoking is something negative, not positive, and this will provide justification for banning it. If the government decides to ban it, then obeying this law will become obligatory and smoking will become *Haram*. And Allah knows best.

Smoking Is Enemy No. 1 for Female Hormones

In order to prove themselves equal to men, women took the fatal step of resorting to smoking. It starts with a few puffs on their husbands' cigarettes and ends with bad habits including the *Shisha* ("hubbly-bubbly"), marijuana, and even sitting in coffee-shops on streetsides.

Although this phenomenon has had serious social and educational impacts on the new generation which is growing up in an environment with no good examples to follow, what concerns us here is sounding the alarm for women who will pay a much greater price than men for smoking. Even worse than that, women are not the only victims of smoking; their children, who are their most precious assets, will never be safe from it either.

The list of diseases proved by

scientific research to be the result of women smoking is continually increasing. It includes serious diseases such as heart disease, angina, and cancers of various types. Even worse than that, smoking plays havoc on female hormones, which means that the woman gradually changes into something that is neither male nor female. As for her children, they are affected by allergies and lung problems from their earliest days, because they stay close to their mothers for a long time.

Forty percent of female students smoke

Despite these disturbing facts, a study prepared by the National Center of Social Research and Criminology in Egypt in 2001 discovered astounding facts. Results showed that 40 percent of female students who took part in the study, of whom there were 7,255 students, smoke more than 20 cigarettes a day.

This was despite the fact that the oldest of these students was no more than 20 years old.

The study examined the occasions on which the students first smoked, and found out that gatherings with female and male friends accounted for 21 percent of the causes for starting to smoke. Sixteen percent of the subjects started to smoke for reasons of imitating others or curiosity, or for the sake of appearance. Five percent started to smoke as a way of coping with problems that they were facing, and 9 percent said that they did it on happy occasions.

The latest medical research in this field suggests that smoking increases a woman's chance of developing cancer of the lung and cervix; it also leads to an increased risk of breast cancer. Women who smoke are also more likely to experience early menopause and infertility.

Some studies have shown that 29 percent of cases of death due to cervical cancer occurred among female smokers. A pregnant woman who smokes faces the risk of miscarriage, defects in the placenta, premature delivery, difficulties in labor, delivering a stillborn child,

birth defects, and lung ailments of the newborn and the risk of early miscarriage.

After birth, the mother's smoking may cause bronchial catarrh, anaemia, chest and skin allergies, vomiting, and lack of appetite, developmental delays, speech problems and lower intelligence in her child.

A look at reasons for smoking

It is strange that despite these dangers, the number of women smokers is continually rising. Day after day, women are turning to smoking and trying new kinds of cigarettes that are more dangerous than the ordinary type.

We asked a number of women for the reason why they started to smoke. L.N., a government employee, told us: "I have smoked since I graduated from university. My family and friends know about that and it is not a secret. I believe that it is my right so long as it is not done in a bad way or an exaggerated way. Smoking is not bad or shameful as long as it is not done inappropriately, and a woman does not smoke when she is pregnant or in front of her children."

Lubna, a housewife, agrees with her, saying, "Smoking is not *Haram*, it is a personal choice. A lot of women have started to smoke cigarettes and also the *Shisha*. Why do we get angry with a woman and not with a man who does what he likes?" She adds, "Just as smoking has known effects, it also has guidelines that the wise person pays attention to. A person who has heart problems or allergies should not smoke, and those around him should respect that and not pressure him to smoke. There are different types of cigarettes nowadays and there are types which contain less nicotine. And we should not forget that cigarettes are not alcohol so there is no need to launch this strong campaign against them."

K.S., a 33-year-old journalist, says, "I began to smoke with my friend while studying; when I was a student in secondary school. It began as innocent curiosity, but since then I have not given up smoking; rather my appetite for it increased when I began frequenting hair dressers in whose shops most girls smoked without any worries." She adds, "Because of smoking my first engagement was canceled, because my fiancé hated cigarettes and I refused to give them up. But after that I got married to a smoker. But I will admit that my health has been affected severely by this bad habit."

M.H., a student, says, "I was impressed by a certain doctor because she is educated and defends the cause of women and demands equality with men. I used to see her smoking a lot in every university lecture and conference that I attended, and gradually I found myself following her example."

By studying the views quoted above, we can see the extent to which women smokers are influenced by Western secular ideas and values which give them a false concept of women's freedom that contradicts the principles of Islam and the sound human nature (*Fitrah*) that Allah, Most High, has created in humans.

Harmful effects

Concerning the harmful effects of smoking on women, Dr. Mahir 'Imran, a professor of gynaecology and obstetrics in the Medical Faculty of Ain Shams University in Cairo, says: There are harmful effects of smoking that affect women only and not men, such as the effect of smoking on fertility, on pregnancy and on the unborn child, and even on her grandchildren. Studies confirm that smoking is the antithesis of the true concept of feminity. It has been proved, first of all, that nicotine and some other substances contained in cigarettes of which there are over 650 chemical substances affect the female hormone estrogens in all parts of the body. Smoking stops the hormones that regulate the menstrual cycle from working, and cause atrophy of the cells of the ovary which excrete estrogens, which is the hormone of complete female maturity. A woman cannot move from childhood to the stage of maturity if estrogens is not present. Hence, the signs of feminity disappear and there is no

menstruation or ovulation.

Smoking reduces the benefit of tissues in the human body that rely on this hormone, of which there are many, such as the breasts, skin, internal and external genital organs, bones, heart, veins and memory centres in the brain.

Dr. 'Imran adds that studies confirm that smoking reduces the number of eggs, which makes a woman reach menopause early and age prematurely.

Lethal smoke

The following are some statistics and newspaper reports:

Al-Sharq Al-Awsat: A report from the World Health Organization expects that by the beginning of 2020, 10 million people will be killed by smoking annually, of whom 7 million live in the Third World, as the percentage of people who smoke in the developing world is increasing by 2.7 percent annually, whereas the rate of smoking is decreasing by 1.8 percent in developed countries.

The organization estimates in its report, published on the occasion of International Anti-Smoking Day, that the number of smokers in the world is approximately 1,100,000,000, of whom about 800 million live in developing countries. It puts the number of female smokers in developing countries at 7 percent and the number of men at 48 percent. Tobacco is regarded as a global monopoly in which a handful of companies spend $4billion annually on advertising to promote this health-damaging product.

The report warns of the danger of smoking which led to the death of one in twelve people in 1990. In 2020, smoking will cause the death of one in every seven people. The report indicates that the death ratio of smokers aged between 35 and 69 will be three times higher than among non-smokers, as scientific research has proved that smoking is responsible for 90 percent of lung cancer deaths worldwide, and 30 percent of all cases of cancer.

Smoking is regarded as responsible for 40 percent of cases of low birth weight in infants in Western countries; it is also responsible for premature births due to weakness, and it increases by 30 percent the risk of the infant being born weighing less than 3.5 kg to a mother who smokes.

American cigarettes contain a high ratio of carcinogens

American scientists themselves say that American cigarettes contain a higher level of chemical cancer-causing substances than other cigarettes that are produced in foreign countries.

The Center for Disease Control, based in Atlanta, Georgia, compared the level of nitrosamine, which causes cancer, in American cigarettes that were chosen for their availability all over the world, with the levels of this substance in local cigarettes in thirteen other countries, including Germany and Japan.

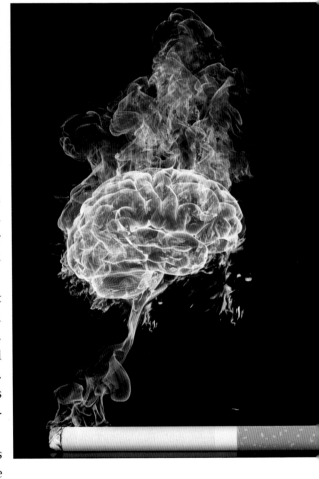

The Center found that the levels of this chemical in local cigarettes in 11 countries was much lower than in the American cigarettes; in some cases it was less than half.

David Ashley, who carried out the research, told the Associated Press news agency the results, which were published in the Journal of Nicotine and Tobacco Research, may indicate that the manufacturers could reduce the levels of cancer-causing nitrosamine in cigarettes.

America's Phillip Morris Company, which produces these cigarettes, says that it is working with American tobacco farmers to reduce the amount of cancer-causing substances in their products.

Brendan McCormack, the company spokesman, says, "We are trying

to find a way to reduce the harmful effects connected with our product by lowering the level of harmful ingredients that smokers inhale."

But the Center for Disease Control warns that nitrosamine is not the only cancer-causing substance that is found in cigarettes, and it says that reducing the level of one substance alone will not guarantee that the harmful effects of smoking are reduced.

Anti-smoking groups say that the study proves that the tobacco industry has only done a little to remove harmful chemical substances from cigarettes.

Twenty-three thousand people die as a result of smoking every year in Saudi Arabia, which is the fourth largest importer of cigarettes in the world.

> **Al-Watan:** A health report has disclosed that the number of deaths resulting from smoking in Saudi Arabia has been estimated at 23 thousand annually, at a time when it is regarded as the fourth largest importer of cigarettes in the world, with sales of 15 billion cigarettes worth an estimated 636 million Saudi riyals. The city of Riyadh alone accounts for about 35 percent of the total Saudi cigarette consumption.

The Health Minister, Hamad Al-Mani', said in a statement issued on the occasion of Saudi Arabia's joining other countries in celebrating International Anti-Smoking Day, under the slogan "Movies Without Tobacco", "The Ministry has set up anti-smoking clinics in all areas of Saudi Arabia to limit the spread of smoking and to help young smokers to give up the habit. He pointed out that this problem needs combined efforts from both official and community-based sources, working on the individual and community levels, to fight this danger which is clearly threatening the well-being of society."

On the other hand, the supervisor of the Health Ministry's anti-smoking program confirmed that more than 55 anti-smoking clinics have been operating with remarkable human and technical resources, offering their services for free to all smokers who want to quit smoking. They have helped tens of thousands of smokers, of whom 35 percent have managed to quit it. He added that between 5 and 10 percent of smokers in Saudi Arabia are aged 15-17 years.

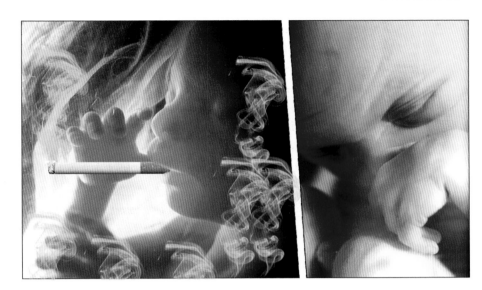

Effects of smoking on the fetus

The effects of smoking on the fetus are innumerable. Dr. 'Imran also spoke of them, saying, The fetus is completely dependent upon the nutrition and oxygen that reach it via the placenta, and on the number of red blood cells that bring the oxygen that the fetus needs. The contents of cigarettes lead to narrowing of the blood vessels in the placenta, and toxic carbon monoxide takes the place of oxygen in the red blood cells, which fail to supply the fetus with the oxygen it needs. Hence, it is confirmed that children who are born to mothers who smoke have a lower birth weight than children of non-smokers. Smoking also increases the risk of premature birth due to weakness.

The most recent medical research during the past year indicates that there is a strong relationship between smoking and cervical cancer, which proves that the woman who smokes increases her risk of developing this kind of malignant tumour.

Causes of early aging

Dr. Muhammad Al-Tahami, assistant teacher of dermatology and venereal diseases in the Ain Shams University, says: Smoking has a major impact of destroying the youthful vitality of the skin and the

appearance of signs of early aging. That is because the skin loses collagen due to smoking, which breaks down collagen. Smoking also increases the number of free radicals, which reduces the levels of the enzymes which are responsible for defining their quantity. As a result of the increase in levels of these free radicals, signs of aging appear on the skin.

He adds that smoking is behind 75 percent of deaths with no previous symptoms, 78 percent of heart attacks, 70 percent of angina cases, and 68 percent of lung cancer cases, 14 percent of cancers of the larynx, 12 percent of mouth cancers and 5 percent of bladder cancers.

Evidence of the jurists that smoking is *Haram*

Among the Hanafis, those that were of the view that smoking is *Haram* include Sheikh Al-Sharnablali Al-Masiri and the author of *Al-Durr Al-Muntaqa*, who quoted Ibn 'Aabidin as saying that it is *Makrooh* in the sense of being virtually *Haram* according to Sheikh 'Abdur Rahman Al-'Imadi. Among the Malikis, Salim Al-Sanhoori, Ibrahim Al-Laqani, Muhammad Ibn 'Abdul Kareem Al-Fakkoon, Khalid Ibn Ahmad, Ibn Hamdoon and others said that it is *Haram*.

Among the Shaf'is, Najm Al-Deen Al-Ghizzi, Al-Qalyoobi, Ibn

'Allan and others said that it is *Haram*.

Among the Hanbalis, Sheikh Ahmad Al-Bahooti and some of the Najdi scholars said that it is *Haram*.

Among these scholars are some who wrote books about the prohibition of smoking, such as Al-Laqani, Al-Qalyoobi, Muhammad Ibn 'Abdul Kareem Al-Fakkoon and Ibn 'Allan. Those who say that it is *Haram* quote the following as evidence:

* Smoking causes intoxication at first, quickly leading to complete fogginess of the mind. Then each time a person smokes that effect reduces gradually, until it no longer has an effect on him; rather, he feels a sense of elevation that he finds better than intoxication. Or what is meant by intoxication is that which befogs the mind even if it is not accompanied by a "high". Undoubtedly this happens to the one who smokes for the first time, and it is for this reason that it is *Najis* (impure), the one who consumes it should be given a *Hadd* punishment and it is *Haram* whether in small quantities or large.

* If it is said that it does not cause intoxication, nevertheless it causes relaxation for the user, so it is like alcohol with regard to giving a "high". Umm Salamah, may Allah be pleased with her, said, "The Messenger of Allah, peace and blessings of Allah be upon him, forbade all intoxicants and relaxants." [Narrated by Ahmad and Abu Dawood, and it is *Saheeh*, apart from the phrase "and relaxants" which is *dha'eef* (weak).]

The scholars said, "A relaxant is that which causes relaxation in the limbs, making one feel weak and tired. The Hadith of Umm Salamah is sufficient evidence and proof that it is *Haram*."

But according to this it is not *Najis*, and the one who consumes it is not to be given a *Hadd* punishment, but a small amount is forbidden just as a large amount is, so as to avoid its effects, because its effects may occur with the smallest amount of it, and protecting the mind is one of the five principles that scholars are agreed upon.

Smoking leads to harm affecting one's body, mind and wealth. It damages the heart, weakens the body and gives the skin a yellowish pallor. Accumulation of smoke in the body causes disease and sickness,

such as coughing that leads to tuberculosis. Continued smoking leads to blackening of whatever the smoke gets to, and causes a rise in temperature, so it becomes a chronic, fatal sickness. Therefore it is included in the Verse:

"And do not kill yourselves." (Soorah An-Nisa', 4:29)

It blocks the veins and prevents nutrition reaching the farthest reaches of the body, so the smoker may die suddenly.

Then it was said: Doctors in the East and in the West agree that it is harmful and evil, and they have warned against it. Sheikh 'Aleesh said, "Some of those who interacted with the British told me that they did not bring tobacco to the Muslim world until after all doctors had agreed that they should avoid smoking and should limit it to a few occasions that would not cause harm. So they told them not to continue smoking, but they told them to sell tobacco to the Muslims so as to harm them."

"If there were nothing more to it than this, it should motivate the rational person to avoid it. The Messenger of Allah, peace and blessings of Allah be upon him, said: "That which is lawful is plain and that which is unlawful is plain, and between the two of them there are doubtful matters about which not many people know. Thus, he who avoids doubtful matters clears himself in regard to his religion and his honor, but he who falls into doubtful matters falls into that which is unlawful, like the shepherd who pastures around a sanctuary, all but grazing therein. Truly every king has a sanctuary, and truly Allah's sanctuary is His prohibitions. Truly in the body there is a morsel of flesh which, if it is sound, all the body is sound and which, if it is corrupt, all of it will be corrupt. Truly it is the heart." (Narrated by Al-Bukhari and Muslim)

In modern references there is proof that smoking is harmful.

Smoking is also extravagance and a waste of money. Sheikh 'Aleesh said, "If the jurists were asked about smoking in relation to the legal condition of 'foolishness' which authorizes preventing a person from disposing of his own wealth constitutes spending it on pleasures and whims and desires, they would not hesitate to say that this principle must also be applied in the case of the one who is addicted to smoking. Look at what results from wasting money on smoking, which puts a strain on the poor and needy, and deprives them of charity because money is spent on smoking instead. Those who smoke are willingly giving money to the enemies of Islam – millions of dollars every day – and withholding it from the Muslims' interests and failing to help the needy."

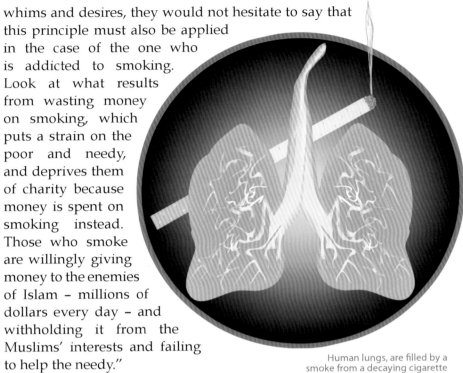

Human lungs, are filled by a smoke from a decaying cigarette

An imperial order was issued by the Ottoman Caliph of the time – based on a *Fatwa* of the scholars of his era – forbidding use of tobacco, punishing smokers and burning whatever tobacco was found.

One of the reasons why it is forbidden is that it is rebelling against the authority of the ruler, because following his commands is obligatory unless it is *Haram* to do so (i.e. if he commands something that is contrary to Islamic rulings), and going against his commands is *Haram*.

The smell of tobacco is foul and offensive, and every offensive smell is disallowed. The smell of tobacco is worse than the smell of onions and garlic, and it is narrated that those who have eaten these two things should not be allowed to enter the mosque. There is a difference between a foul smell and an unpleasant smell. Onions and garlic have an unpleasant smell but it is not foul; the smell of tobacco is foul.

Those who claim to use it for medicinal purposes do not use it as medicine is used; they go too far, to the extent of enjoying it and

reveling in it. They claim to use it as a medicine as a coverup in order to reach their hidden aim of "play" and enjoying its intoxicating effects. The Hanafi view is that it is *Haram*, and they defined "play" as doing something for no valid purpose, and "foolishness" as doing something for no purpose whatsoever. And Allah knows best.

Signing a global declaration against smoking

On Wednesday 22/3/1424 A.H., more than one hundred and ninety countries ratified the first global declaration against smoking which included a complete ban on tobacco adverts, and aimed at putting an end to a habit that kills more than five million people every year.

Of the countries that attended the annual general meeting of the World Health Organization, 192 agreed to adopt the framework for fighting smoking that was previously agreed upon last March, after years of difficult negotiations.

According to this agreement, the signatory nations committed to fight the destructive consequences of tobacco consumption and exposure.

Gro Harlem Brundtland, the general director of the World Health Organization, said, "We are working to save the lives of billions of people and to protect the health of people of future generations. It is a historical moment."

The agreement obliges the signatory nations to ban advertisements and impose strict restrictions on advertising campaigns, sponsorship and propagation of tobacco for five years. It also lays down new guidelines for health warnings on cigarette boxes, and includes a special recommendation for increasing taxes on tobacco products, and launching campaigns against tobacco smuggling, as well as other procedures.

The agreement states that the spread of the tobacco plague is regarded as an international problem with dire consequences for public health, which requires comprehensive, suitable and effective international effort. (A Reuters report)

✻✻✻✻✻

Chapter: 17

Beware of the Two Things That Incur Curses

Dr. Raja' Mahmoud Malyani

*Associate Professor and Ph.D.
in Medical Microbiology, University of London*

The Prophet, peace and blessings of Allah be upon him, said:

> "Beware of the two things that incur curses." They said, "What are the two things that incur curses, O Messenger of Allah?" He said: "Relieving oneself in the road used by people or in the places where they seek shade." (Narrated by Ahmad and Muslim)

> And he said: "No one of you should urinate in standing water then wash himself with it." (Agreed upon)

It was narrated from Jabir, may Allah be pleased with him:

> "That the Messenger of Allah, peace and blessings of Allah be upon him, forbade urinating in stagnant water." (Narrated by Muslim)

And he said: "When one of you wakes up, let him not dip his hand into his (water) vessel until he washes it three times, because he does not know where his hand spent the night." (Agreed upon)

And he said:

"When one of you drinks, let him not breathe into the vessel, and when he goes to relieve himself, let him not touch his penis with his right hand or wipe his behind with his right hand."

It was narrated that Abul-Ghadiyah Al-Yamami said,

"I came to Madinah and the envoy of Katheer Ibn Al-Salt came and called them but no one got up except Abu Hurairah, may Allah be pleased with him, and five others, and I was one of them. They went and ate, then Abu Hurairah, may Allah be pleased with him, came and washed his hand, then he said: 'By Allah, O people of the mosque, you are disobeying Abul-Qasim, peace and blessings of Allah be upon him.'" (Narrated by Ahmad)

If we look through the microscope or from the viewpoint of microbiology we will see the great benefits that we gain by following the teachings outlined above and we will see the wisdom behind these narrations. Science has proved the secrets behind these Prophetic teachings by means of discoveries which prove the relationship between the narrations quoted and many numbers of germs that cause disease. We now realize that the faeces of both healthy and sick human beings contain various kinds of germs in huge numbers that may cause many diseases if one goes against the teachings of the Prophet, peace and blessings of Allah be upon him. Among these germs are millions of bacteria, viruses, parasites and funguses, some of which causes disease and some of which may cause disease under certain circumstances.

Colon bacteria present in the intestines and faeces

In addition to the above, faeces may also contain worms that cause disease, which may be at different stages of development. Obviously many of the microbes that are expelled with the faeces, both those that cause disease and those that do not, may cause contamination of the surrounding area, food and water. The hands may also be contaminated with some of these faeces which contain disease-causing microbes that cannot be seen with the naked eye. The infection may be transmitted from one person to another, and thus the disease spreads. It is sufficient to point out here that some serious diseases are transmitted by swallowing food or water that is contaminated via the "faecal-oral route". For example (and this is not an exhaustive list): typhoid fever, cholera, dysentery, hepatitis, polio

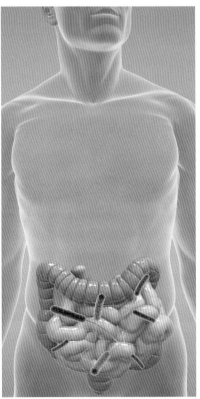

colon infection

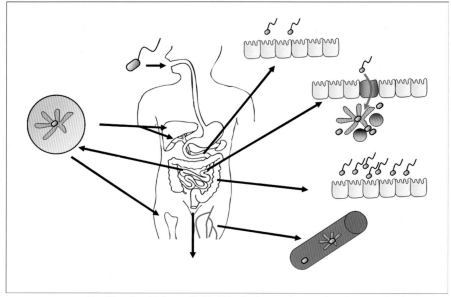

The lifestyle of Salmonella Typhi in the human host and implications for diagnostic

and intestinal problems such as severe diarrhoea and vomiting.

Let us look in detail at one of the microbes mentioned above, the *Salmonella typhi* bacteria, which causes typhoid fever, also known as enteric fever. Infection occurs when food or drink contaminated with the bacteria is swallowed, and the infectious dose (the number of bacteria that causes sickness) is usually large. Because of the sensitive nature of *Salmonella typhi*, sickness occurs after nine days, i.e., the incubation period may be long or short depending on the number of bacteria swallowed, in addition to other factors such as the strain of salmonella, and the person's immunity and general state of health.

In general, the incubation period varies between 5 and 14 days, and may be as long as 21 days. After swallowing this number of bacteria in the contaminated food, it passes through the stomach and reaches the small intestine, where the bacteria attach themselves to the wall of the intestine, then they penetrate the lining of the intestine and are absorbed by cells which are not usually able to kill the bacteria, which is able to multiply inside the cells. This method is regarded as one of the most important factors in causing salmonella typhoid. After the bacteria have gained control of the cells, they travel via the lymph glands to the blood stream, causing bacteraemia (the presence of bacteria in the blood). Then they spread to the liver, gall bladder, spleen, kidneys and bone marrow. During this stage, there is a rise in body temperature, and the symptoms of typhoid fever occur, such as headache, lethargy, a slight cough in some cases, insomnia, stomach pain and diarrhoea, or sometimes constipation. Sometimes there is a rash in the form of small pink spots (rose spots) on the stomach.

What concerns us here is the fact that throughout these stages, the *Salmonella typhi* bacteria is expelled with the faeces in huge numbers, and is sometimes expelled with the urine too. It is well-known that there is a certain percentage of patients who continue to carry the bacteria for

many years after recovery (chronic carriers) as it remains present in two places. The first is the gall bladder, which is the usual case, where the bacteria travels from the gall bladder to the intestines and is then expelled with the faeces, and the second place is the center of the kidney, whence it is expelled with the urine.

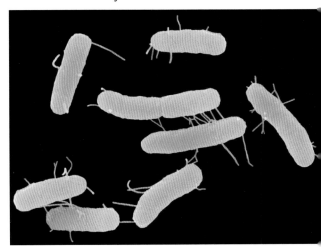

Salmonella typhi bacteria

Hence, the narration of the Prophet, peace and blessings of Allah be upon him, represent the pinnacle of science and knowledge, because he is the one who forbade us to defecate in the street, and he forbade us to urinate in standing water, because the faeces of the sick person and carrier of the germs would contaminate the soil, as the urine that carries the germs would contaminate the water and the soil, especially since *Salmonella typhi* can survive in soil and faeces for six weeks and in water for four weeks at least.

The Prophet, peace and blessings of Allah be upon him, also commanded us to wash our hands and not to wipe ourselves with our right hands. It has now been proved scientifically that most cases of food poisoning, typhoid and dysentery are caused by food handlers

who carry the germs that cause sickness and do not pay attention to cleanliness and following the *Sunnah*.

The most famous germ carrier was a cook called Mary in the United States. It was discovered that she was a carrier of the *Salmonella typhi* bacteria, which was expelled in her faeces, and she caused the spread of typhoid fever to the members of the households where she worked, and even in hospitals. At the time, she was followed by a public health officer who noticed the connection during her presence as a cook at places where typhoid fever spread. He asked her to undergo some medical exams but she refused and fled the area. After that, some cases of typhoid fever appeared in a public hospital, and the public health officer went himself to that hospital to study the source of the infection. He was astonished to see that same cook, Mary, working there in the hospital kitchen under a different name. The story ended with a court case, in which Mary was ordered to stop working as a cook and undergo the necessary medical tests. From that time onward this cook was known by the name of Typhoid Mary.

The outbreak of typhoid fever that appeared in 1964 in the Scottish city of Aberdeen was amazing because it resulted from eating food from imported tins that had been contaminated at their source. It was discovered that after sterilization, the tins had been placed in a river near the factory to cool them off. Reports at the time explained that the river was contaminated by open sewers, and that the *Salmonella* bacteria had entered the tins through small holes because they were not sealed properly. *Subhan Allah!* A nearby river could contaminate the tins that were placed in it to cool them off, so how about stagnant water? Yes, the Prophet, peace and blessings of Allah be upon him, indeed spoke the truth; he was truly the Unlettered Prophet, and he truly spoke not of his own whims and desires. And Allah knows best.

*****

roundworms

Dogs, Germs and Soil

It was narrated that Abu Hurairah, may Allah be pleased with him, said, the Messenger of Allah, peace and blessings of Allah be upon him, said:

"The purification of the vessel of one of you, if it is licked by a dog, is to wash it seven times, the first time with soil." (Narrated by Muslim)

It was narrated that Ibn Al-Mughaffal said, the Messenger of Allah, peace and blessings of Allah be upon him, enjoined killing dogs, then he said:

"What is the matter with them and dogs?" Then he granted a

concession with regard to hunting dogs and sheepdogs, and said: "If the dog licks the vessel, then wash it seven times and rub it the eighth time with soil." (Narrated by Muslim)

The words, "if the dog licks the vessel", means if it drinks from it with its tongue.

It has been proved scientifically that dogs transmit several serious diseases, because there lives in the dog's intestines a worm called the roundworm, the eggs of which are expelled with the faeces. When a dog licks its behind, the eggs are transferred to its tongue and then are transmitted to the vessels, plates and hands of its owner, from where they enter the stomach and intestines. Then the skin of the egg disintegrates and the larva emerges, which reaches the blood and mucus, and travels via them to all parts of the body, especially the liver, as it is the main cleansing organ in the body.

Then it grows in the organ that it has entered and forms a sac filled with larvae and a clear liquid. This sickness is called water sac disease. Its symptoms depend on the part of the body affected, the most dangerous of which is the brain or heart muscle. There is no remedy for it apart from surgery.

There is another disease which is transmitted by dogs, namely

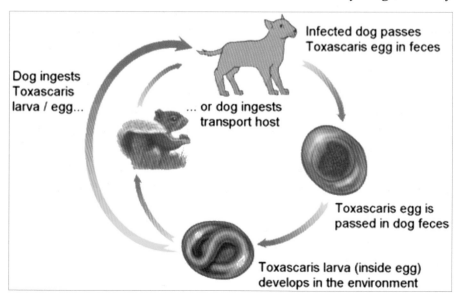

Infected dog passes Toxascaris egg in feces

Dog ingests Toxascaris larva / egg...

... or dog ingests transport host

Toxascaris egg is passed in dog feces

Toxascaris larva (inside egg) develops in the environment

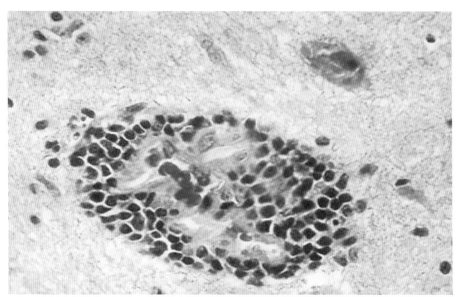

rabies-in-dogs

rabies which is caused by a virus which affects the dog first, then it is transmitted to humans via the dog's saliva, if it bites the human or licks a wound on the human's body.

So the benefits of dogs are limited to some humans, but their harm affects everyone. Hence, the Prophet, peace and blessings of Allah be upon him, enjoined killing dogs. Then he granted a concession with regard to dogs used for hunting, farming and guarding livestock, because there is a need for them.

At the time of the Prophet, peace and blessings of Allah be upon him, water sac disease was of course unknown, and it was not known that dogs were its source. As for rabies, they called the dog that was affected by it a "vicious dog".

In modern times, scientists tested soil from graves to find out what germs it contained. They were expecting to find a lot of harmful germs, because many humans die of infectious diseases. But they did not find any trace of those harmful germs. So they concluded that soil has the ability to kill harmful germs. Were it not for that, the danger could have spread and become a serious problem. Moreover, the germs that are contained in a dogs' saliva cannot be killed or removed except by

rubbing them with soil. In the American University in Lebanon, tests were carried out concerning this issue, and the result was as we have mentioned. The Prophet, peace and blessings of Allah be upon him, stated this fact in his narration more than fourteen centuries before they found it out.

The difference between dogs and cats

Is the dog regarded as one of the animals that transmit contagious diseases? The dog carries many contagious diseases. It carries more than fifty parasitic diseases, many of which are found in its saliva. But what about cats? Do they share this characteristic with dogs?

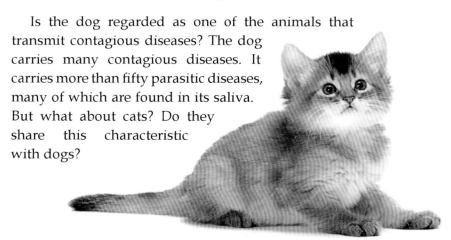

The cat is regarded as the cleanest of animals from a medical point of view, because it does not carry germs and parasites except that which causes just one disease. What is this disease? It is one which, if a person catches it, he will become blind. How does that happen? This disease is found in the cat's faeces, and if another animal eats the faeces, the disease will be transmitted to its body. When that animal is slaughtered and its meat is eaten, the sickness will in turn be transmitted to the human.

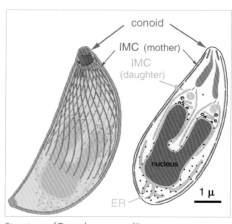

Structure of Toxoplasma gondii

Glory be to the One Who has made this animal inclined to

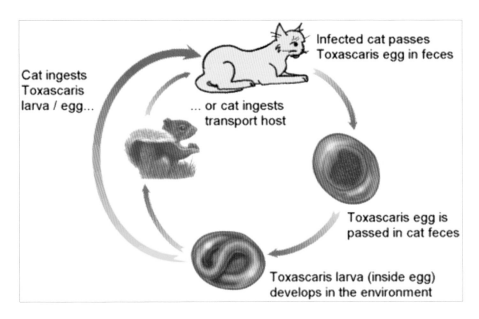

Infected cat passes Toxascaris egg in feces

Cat ingests Toxascaris larva / egg...

... or cat ingests transport host

Toxascaris egg is passed in cat feces

Toxascaris larva (inside egg) develops in the environment

bury its faeces so that other animals will not eat it. Thus it absolves itself from responsibility and is exempted from being treated like dogs, as the Prophet, peace and blessings of Allah be upon him, said concerning cats: "They are not Najis (impure); rather they are among those who go around among you."

The narrator said: "I saw the Messenger of Allah, peace and blessings of Allah be upon him, doing *Wudhoo'* with its leftover water (i.e., water from which a cat had drunk)." (Narrated by the five; Al-Tirmidhi said, a *saheeh hasan Hadith*)

[*Al-Haqa'iq Al-Tibbiyah Fil-Islam*]

*****

The Mosquito and That Which Is Smaller Than It

Allah, The Exalted, says:

﴿ إِنَّ ٱللَّهَ لَا يَسۡتَحۡيِۦٓ أَن يَضۡرِبَ مَثَلٗا مَّا بَعُوضَةٗ فَمَا فَوۡقَهَاۚ فَأَمَّا ٱلَّذِينَ ءَامَنُواْ فَيَعۡلَمُونَ أَنَّهُ ٱلۡحَقُّ مِن رَّبِّهِمۡۖ وَأَمَّا ٱلَّذِينَ كَفَرُواْ فَيَقُولُونَ مَاذَآ أَرَادَ ٱللَّهُ بِهَٰذَا مَثَلٗاۘ يُضِلُّ بِهِۦ كَثِيرٗا وَيَهۡدِي بِهِۦ كَثِيرٗاۚ وَمَا يُضِلُّ بِهِۦٓ إِلَّا ٱلۡفَٰسِقِينَ ﴾

"Verily, Allah is not ashamed to set forth a parable even of a mosquito or so much more when it is bigger (or less when it is smaller) than it. And as for those who believe, they know that it is the Truth from their Lord, but as for those who disbelieve, they say: 'What did Allah intend by this parable?' By it He misleads many, and many He guides thereby. And He misleads thereby only those who are Fasiqoon (the rebellious, disobedient to Allah)." (Soorah Al-Baqarah, 2:26)

The Ministry of Health in the Kingdom of Saudi Arabia announced on 17 September 2000 that 16 people had died as the result of contracting Rift Valley fever in the Jazan region. The World Health Organization confirmed the news. At that time, the Kingdom had begun an awareness campaign and took protective measures that were focused principally on getting rid of the main vector which carried the virus, namely the mosquito. Once again it was proved how significant the mosquito is and how dangerous it is to human life, even if people regard it as insignificant because it is so small.

The mosquito transmits several types of serious viruses and parasites that affect humans and animals, and it is behind several waves of epidemics that have killed millions. Although it is so small, the mosquito is not to be taken lightly; rather it is very significant because of its destructive effects and the diseases that it causes. Science has not discovered something similar to it or even more dangerous, despite the fact that there are smaller micro-organisms, such as parasites, fungi, bacteria and viruses.

Mankind has regarded the mosquito as insignificant throughout centuries because of its small size, but the Qur'an denounced them for thinking little of it in miraculously eloquent words that point to its importance, using it as a parable to be heeded before its role in transmitting disease was known, and before the discovery of other beings which also pose a danger because of the diseases that they cause. The Qur'an challenges man with what is even smaller than it, which is indicative of the care, power and knowledge of the secrets of all of creation that Allah, the Exalted, possesses.

Comments of the *Mufassireen* (exegetes):

The Verse confirms the miraculous nature of the Qur'an and challenges mankind thereby, because it is a continuation of the previous Verses which praise this Book and describe those who are guided

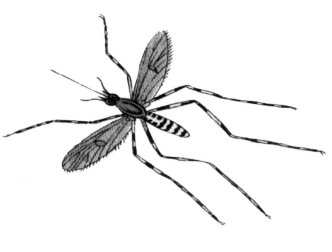

by it and condemns those who turn away from it. The way in which it is connected to the previous Verses is proof of the miraculous nature of the Qur'an, because the pronoun in the phrase "it is the Truth" refers primarily to the word "parable", but it may also refer to the Qur'an, because the truth is in accordance with reality and this is the nature of the Qur'an, because Allah, the Almighty, says:

﴿ سَنُرِيهِمْ ءَايَٰتِنَا فِى ٱلْءَافَاقِ وَفِىٓ أَنفُسِهِمْ حَتَّىٰ يَتَبَيَّنَ لَهُمْ أَنَّهُ ٱلْحَقُّ ﴾

"We will show them Our Signs in the universe, and in their own selves, until it becomes manifest to them that this (the Qur'an) is the truth." (Soorah Fussilat, 41:53)

Even though the mosquito is so small that people regarded it as insignificant before its danger was discovered, Allah, Most High, has given it many faculties so that it cannot be eradicated easily and no one can defend himself against it, not even the greatest of tyrants. Concerning the words of Allah,

﴿ إِنَّ ٱللَّهَ لَا يَسْتَحْىِۦٓ أَن يَضْرِبَ مَثَلًا مَّا بَعُوضَةً فَمَا فَوْقَهَا ﴾

"Verily, Allah is not ashamed to set forth a parable even of a mosquito or so much more when it is bigger (or less when it is smaller) than it."

Qatadah said, "This means, Allah is not ashamed to speak the truth, i.e., He does not refrain from setting forth a parable of a mosquito."

Abu Ishaq said concerning the words,

﴿ وَٱضۡرِبۡ لَهُم مَّثَلًا ﴾

"And put forward to them a similitude." (Soorah Ya Seen, 36:13).

"This means, tell them."

Al-Jawhari said concerning the words,

﴿ ضَرَبَ ٱللَّهُ مَثَلًا ﴾

"Allah sets forth an example." (Soorah Al-Tahreem 66:10).

"This means, described and explained." In the commentary on *Nuzum Al-Faseeh* it says, "It means quoting it or mentioning it as an example and as a concept that the speaker wants to convey."

What the Verse means is that Allah does not regard anything as too insignificant to use as a parable, even if it is as small as a mosquito. What the foolish, stubborn and argumentative people objected to and

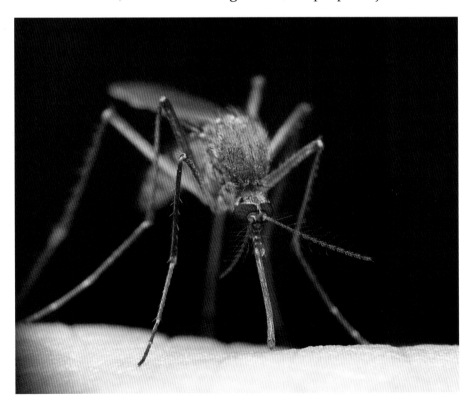

found strange is nothing to be objected to at all. Abu Hayyan said, "He created it in the most perfect manner, gave it the most perfect form, and manifested many great wisdoms in it despite its small size, like those that He manifested in the elephant which is so huge. Although it is small and weak, the mosquito is well-formed and so subtly made that it is impossible to describe it in detail. Despite all that, it can use the thorn of its proboscis to penetrate the skin of a water buffalo and elephant, to which it is guided without any help, which is something that man is unable to do."

Al-Khazin said, "The mosquito is very small and has a hollow proboscis; although it is so small its proboscis can penetrate the skin of an elephant, water buffalo or camel, and it penetrates so deeply that the camel may die from one bite. It is along similar lines that they said: The mosquito can harm the kings on their thrones."

It is regarded as insignificant by those who see it, yet it can still approach a king and annoy him; he cannot ward it off, it may bite him and cut into his skin using the spear of its proboscis. It will defeat you even if you have power and strength; it will shed your blood even if you have weapons and armies at your disposal. It defeats people of resolve even though it is weak. Thus Allah, the Exalted, shows us the wonder of His power and our weakness before the weakest of His creation.

Saying that He is not ashamed to mention it is a rebuke to those who look down on it and is indicative of its importance and significance, confirming that Allah, the Almighty, cares for and grants potential to this tiny creature that challenges those who are addressed. If we assume that the word mosquito refers to a parable that is a mosquito and that which is smaller than it, then Allah is confirming that there is no shame is making a parable of a mosquito and what is smaller in size than it. Thus the meaning is that Allah is denouncing those who think little of it and He is taking it as an example among other harmful creatures that are equally dangerous. Thus the Verse highlights the significance of the mosquito and includes other living beings whose harm was not known at the time of Revelation, which may be the same size or bigger or smaller.

From a linguistic point of view, what may be meant is more of the description mentioned in the context in which the comparison is made. In the phrase *Ba'oodah wa ma Fawqaha* (translated here as "a mosquito or so much more when it is bigger or less when it is smaller than it") what is meant is more of the characteristic for which the parable is given, which is smallness and insignificance. So it moves from being insignificant to being more insignificant, i.e., that which is smaller, because what is being highlighted here is smallness. The word *Fawqa* is used in the sense of going further in the description or quality mentioned.

Al-Razi said, "What is meant here is what is smaller. The scholars prefer this view because the point here is to emphasize that Allah does not refrain from using as a parable something insignificant, and in this context what is mentioned later should be more insignificant than what is mentioned first. The smaller a thing is, the more difficult it is to find out about its secrets. If it is very small then no one will have complete knowledge of it except Allah, so using it as a parable is more effective in proving perfect wisdom than using something big as a parable.

If it is said that one thing is above another in smallness, that means that it is smaller, and the excuse of those who interpreted it as meaning that it was bigger was that they did not know that there was anything smaller than a mosquito, and they thought it was the ultimate in smallness and weakness. But the meaning that is highlighted here is smallness and insignificance, and it should not be asked how something smaller than a mosquito can be used as a parable when it is the smallest thing (as they used to think), because the Verse comments on that:

> "And as for those who believe, they know that it is the Truth from their Lord".

This makes them think about it, and when they find out what this verse refers to in detail, their faith and knowledge increases, otherwise they know that it is true even if the truth that it contains and its exact meaning is hidden from them, because they know that Allah, the Exalted, is not setting forth this parable for no reason, rather there is great wisdom in it."

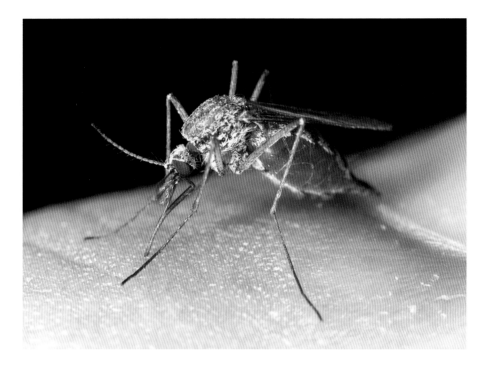

Scientific definition of the mosquito

It is a small insect with two wings (dipteral). The male only feeds on nectar; it does not feed on blood, and it plays no role in biting humans and animals. The female has a mouth that is designed to make a hole in the skin of humans and warm-blooded animals in order to feed on the blood, which is a rich source of protein that is needed to produce eggs. The female secretes a solution from her salivary glands into the wound which leads to swelling and prevents the blood from clotting, so that it flows easily to her mouth. If she is carrying microscopic beings that cause disease, which she acquired from previously biting an infected human or animal, then it is possible that it may be transmitted with her saliva, and thus the disease spreads widely. Hence the problem is not just the annoying buzzing or the bite which may be painful or cause itching and swelling; rather the danger is in the germs transmitted, which may cause a serious or lethal infection, such as the plasmodium parasite; the filarial parasite which causes elephantiasis; the viruses responsible for yellow fever, encephalitis, dengue fever, haemorrhagic fever and Rift Valley fever. Their danger extends to a number of birds and mammals. These diseases also include heartworm disease, which affects dogs in particular, and in rare cases affects humans; it results from infection with a type of filarial parasite.

The mosquito is composed of a head, thorax and abdomen, like other insects. It has three pairs of long, slender legs and a pair of wings, near which is a pair of halteres or small knobbed structures which may appear as undeveloped wings; they are used for balance. There are numerous scales on the veins of the wings which increase the insect's ability to fly. The adult insect lays 100-400 eggs, very few of which actually hatch and complete the lifecycle. The insect matures in 7-10 days in some species. You can expect the mosquito to hatch within two weeks of the eggs being laid when water is available, because water is essential for the eggs to hatch and the larva and pupa to live. The egg may remain dormant for a lengthy period waiting for water. Or the egg may hatch 1-3 days after laying, turning into a larva that in turn remains for a period between 5 days and several weeks before turning into a pupa.

The larva is very active, hence it is called a "wriggler"; it feeds voraciously on algae and organic material in the water and its appetite may be so great that it feeds on other larvae like itself. The larva breathes by means of an air tube near its tail. The pupa does not feed, and when disturbed it makes a spiral movement, hence it is called a "tumbler". The pupa remains for 2-3 days before shedding its cocoon and emerging as an adult insect, and after a short period it prepares for mating.

There are between 3 and 4 million species of insect in the world, among which are more than 2000-3000 species of mosquito spread throughout various climates and environments, so that they have reached every area that is populated by man, stretching from the Equator to the North Pole, from valleys to mountaintops. There are three main types or genera of mosquito, as follows:

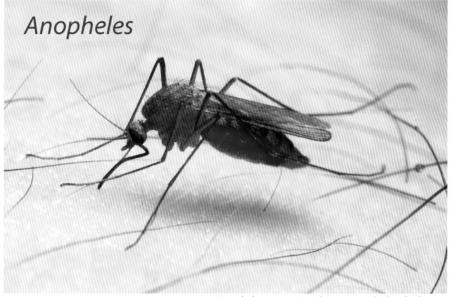

Anopheles mosquito - dangerous vehicle of infection

- **Anopheles**

The *Anopheles* mosquito transmits the malaria and filarial parasites, as well as the virus that causes encephalitis. The insect lays its eggs one by one on the surface of the water. Its life cycle lasts for approximately 18 days, but it may extend to several weeks.

- **Culex**

The *Culex* mosquito transmits the filarial parasite and the virus which causes brain fever. The insect sticks its eggs together in clusters, each of which may contain more than 100 eggs. Its lifecycle lasts 10-14 days.

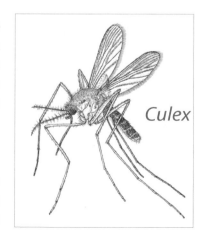

- **Aedes**

The *Aedes* mosquito transmits the viruses that cause yellow fever, dengue fever and brain fever. It differs from the

Culex in some ways such as: the insect has silver scales, and its eggs are able to withstand drought for a long time. Its life cycle is only 10 days, but it may last for many months if there is no water.

The availability of water is essential for the eggs to hatch and the larva and pupa to live. Ponds, swamps and open farmland are the most suitable places for breeding. Some types are able to use salty water or flowing water. In some cases a little water is sufficient, such as left-over rainwater that has accumulated in holes in trees, or even flower nectar if there is no alternative. Mosquitoes usually breed near a source of water, but some types will move far away from their breeding place, so many individual efforts will not succeed in getting rid of them; it needs a concerted national effort to reduce their breeding rates. Most of the regions affected by mosquito-borne diseases are in areas with hot climates. In the winter, some types of mosquito may be dormant, waiting for spring, or there may be eggs waiting for water to become available.

Tropical red mosquito on a green foliage

At the end of the mating season, the rate of disease and waves of epidemics falls. One of the means of protecting oneself when disease is spreading is using artificial or natural repellents, such as derivatives of the *Neem* plant, which contains effective substances such as salannin, or using mosquito netting. In order to limit repeated waves of disease in mosquito-prone regions, it is essential to take many precautions, such as: filling in ponds and swamps, or raising fish that feed on the larvae and pupae in the water, such as the gambosia and guppy.

The mosquito uses its antennae as sensors and it is possible that they are also organs of taste and smell, and sensitive to movement. The little hairs that cover the antennae are denser in the male, which increases his ability and efficiency in detecting females of his type. There is sufficient evidence to believe that the antennae of mosquitoes are very sensitive and efficient as faculties for the reception of sound, like ears, especially since it has been discovered that there are nerve swellings at the base of the antennae which make them respond and turn towards sounds whose frequency is like that of the buzzing of the wings of a female from the same species. For example, a frequency of 384 hertz

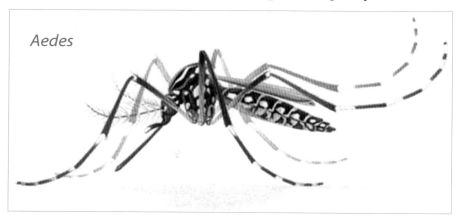

Aedes

(beats per second) distinguishes the mosquito that carries yellow fever, and it may be strongest when the antennae are directed towards the source of the sound. Thus the insect may easily and precisely detect the direction of the sound or small movement, especially when there are two antennae.

The average number of wing beats varies among insects. The minimum is 8 beats per second in some butterflies, and the maximum is 1000 beats per second in some insects. The mosquito is one of the insects that have a rapid wing beat, approximately 600 beats per second. It is the wing beats of the female mosquito that make the well known buzzing sound. Research has proved that it varies from one species to another, and the male is able to easily distinguish the females of his own type and thus propagate generations of the same type. The average wing beat of the female is much less than that of the male, and if it is possible to determine these frequencies in a given area, it is possible to know what species are there. It is even possible to attract males to traps in order to eliminate them, by generating an artificial wing beat like that of the females of the same species. By imitating nature in order to get rid of mosquitoes, it may also be possible to attract females by means of special equipment which releases temperatures and substances like those released by the body, such as carbon dioxide and water vapour in exhaled air, and lactic acid. And lamps may be used at night. If these attempts succeed in populated areas, it will be much safer than chemical insecticides such as DDT, especially since they also kill birds and beneficial insects, and disturb the ecological balance, and in time mosquitoes develop a resistance to them and they become less effective in fighting them.

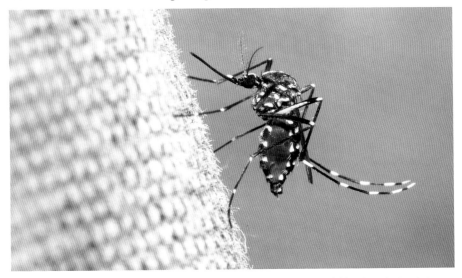

Tiger mosquito (Aedes albopictus) with blood inside the abdomen

Tiny beings threatening mankind

The mosquito's bite may cause local itching, because the body uses a mechanism to get rid of the substance secreted by the mosquito when it bites. But the real danger is the transmission of microscopic beings that cause sickness. It is possible that the mosquito may transmit viruses that attack the human nervous system and cause meningitis, encephalitis

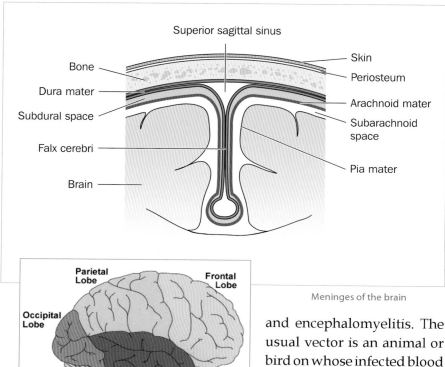

Meninges of the brain

and encephalomyelitis. The usual vector is an animal or bird on whose infected blood the mosquito has fed before attacking a new victim. Encephalitis is a serious disease; its symptoms include stiffness in the neck, difficulty in leaning the neck backward, spasms and other nervous symptoms. Seventy percent of victims die. In yellow fever, the virus attacks the liver cells, which leads to the patient developing a yellow color along with fever; hence the name.

Rift Valley Fever is transmitted by mosquitoes and is caused by a virus that affects livestock and may cause their death; it may also affect humans. The symptoms begin with a fever, sensitivity to light, muscle pain, weakness and maybe bleeding; it may also cause blindness if the patient survives. Encephalitis is one of the complications of the disease. It may be transmitted to humans by handling infected meat or the faeces of a sick animal. The first cases were recorded in Kenya, in the Rift Valley; hence the name. But cases of this sickness have also been recorded in East and South Africa, and most recently (in 2000) in Asian countries such as Yemen and the Kingdom of Saudi Arabia, but the same name is still used for the disease.

Dengue fever is caused by a virus; its symptoms include skin eruptions and severe pain in the joints; hence it is also called break-bone fever. It causes 0.5 million people to be admitted to hospital annually and causes the deaths of thousands. This disease appeared in a more virulent form after the Second World War in South East Asia, where it was called "bleeding knee fever"; it affected children and caused many deaths. It is distinguished by severe bleeding in the mouth and nose, severe thirst and difficulty in breathing. It has now spread to Central America and is spreading north toward the United States. Cases of the sickness have been reported in more than 100 countries. This sickness appears especially in March of every year as the

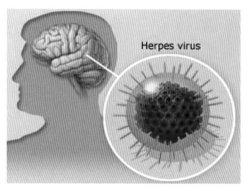

Herpes virus

ENCEPHALITIS

result of the breeding of mosquitoes in hot weather. No vaccine is yet available for this disease, and there is no successful treatment for it. Elephantiasis refers to a swelling in some parts of the body, especially the feet, breasts and scrotal sac. It results from a blockage in the lymphatic vessels caused by the filarial parasite.

The malarial parasite multiplies in the red blood cells and causes paroxysms which are the collective bursting of the affected cells; this happens periodically, every day or every 2-3 days, depending on the type of parasite. The release of a substance that is foreign to the immune system is what causes these main symptoms: shivering and a rise in temperature, then sweating, followed by a respite between attacks. The malarial attack usually lasts between 4 and 10 hours. It starts approximately 8 to 25 days after exposure to mosquitoes. The *Plasmodium falciparum* parasite causes the most severe form of malaria,

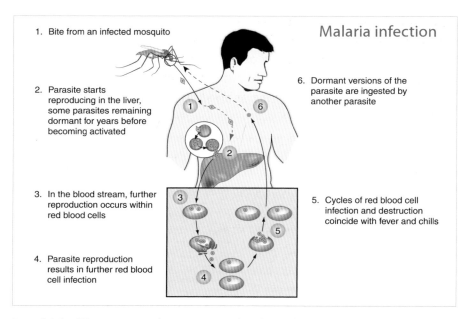

1. Bite from an infected mosquito

Malaria infection

2. Parasite starts reproducing in the liver, some parasites remaining dormant for years before becoming activated

6. Dormant versions of the parasite are ingested by another parasite

3. In the blood stream, further reproduction occurs within red blood cells

5. Cycles of red blood cell infection and destruction coincide with fever and chills

4. Parasite reproduction results in further red blood cell infection

in which 95 percent of cases may lead to death. After a decrease in the number of cases due to use of plant extracts such as quinine and chloroquine, at the end of the twentieth century there emerged complaints that these drugs were no longer so effective, and the number of cases began to rise again, as a result of a new strain of parasites that was resistant to these drugs. This dictated the use of new alternatives. Malaria may also be transmitted when a healthy person uses the same needle that was used by a sick person, without it being sterilized, as happens in the case of drug addicts who use needles. The disease may also be transmitted via drug transfusions. According to a statement made by the World Health Organization, malaria still affects 400 million people annually at the global level, and it kills approximately 2 million people, most of whom are children. Until now there is no effective vaccine against this disease.

AIDS/HIV is basically transmitted via immoral actions, but it may affect a healthy person via transfusion of blood from an infected person. When the disease and its rapid spread were first discovered, mosquitoes were accused of transmitting it, but the AIDS virus cannot live inside the mosquito; hence the insects cannot be transmitting it from one person to another. The malaria virus, on the other hand, can live inside the mosquito for 9-12 days and the encephalitis virus can live for 10-25 days. The AIDS virus is most likely to be digested in the mosquito's stomach within one or two days of a meal of blood, during which time the mosquito does not need any more blood; so transmission via the mouth of a mosquito that did not consume enough blood from the first victim and fed on another is impossible because the numbers of the virus in its mouth is too small and is not sufficient to cause disease in this manner. Hence, the mosquito was declared innocent of this accusation. The diseases that it does cause are sufficient.

Man's helplessness before this challenge

The mosquito is one of the most serious pests that still threaten mankind, because it is (at least until now) impossible to eliminate it. Is it possible to change the mosquito genetically so that it will no longer be harmful to humans and animals and will stop eating meals of blood? Or so that disease will no longer be transmitted via these insects? Or can the genetic material of disease-causing creatures be altered so that they will no longer cause disease? Such audacious questions that are posed by specialists reflect their current helplessness before the strength of mosquitoes and the potential for climate changes which could have an impact on all diseases on the planet, the extent of which no one knows today except Allah alone.

The mosquitoes' menace has reached most advanced countries. For example, in August 1995 there was a sudden spread of aggressive mosquitoes in New Jersey in the US, which inflicted painful bites even in broad daylight. Because of their Asian origin, aggressive bites and striped bodies, they were dubbed "Asian tigers", although their scientific name is Aedes albopictus. They appeared for the first time in the United States in 1985. They began to spread after the Second World War in Hawaii and the Pacific region, but recently they have begun to spread in the US. These mosquitoes multiply rapidly because they do not need large amounts of water for their eggs to hatch, and any

remaining puddles in neglected vessels such as old tires or pools of rain in holes in trees is sufficient. They transmit the viruses that cause dengue fever and encephalitis in humans and animals.

With the disruption in the ecological balance caused by reduction of the size of forests and agricultural areas, and the release of factory smoke containing huge amounts of harmful gases such as carbon dioxide into the air, the temperature of the planet has risen noticeably due to the reflected heat being unable to escape. This is called the greenhouse effect because it is akin to what happens in a greenhouse which is used for growing plants that need extra heat. It is expected that the average global temperature will increase by between 1 and 3.5 degrees Celsius by the beginning of 2100, hence it is expected that the numbers of mosquitoes and the diseases that they cause will also rise, unless decisive protective measures are taken on a global level with the cooperation of the entire human race to confront the menace.

A unique, miraculous Book

Knowledge of the mosquito and living beings that are smaller than it, and their role in the cause and transmission of disease, was impossible before the invention of the microscope. The mosquito's role in transmitting malaria, for example, was unknown until just before the beginning of the twentieth century. Alphonse Laveran discovered the parasite that causes malaria in 1880. In 1897, Sir Roland Ross discovered that it is transmitted by the mosquito. In 1898, an Italian team of researchers confirmed the mosquito's role in the transmission of the disease. Just before the beginning of the twentieth century, there were a number of theories that sought to explain the cause of yellow fever. In 1881, Carlos Finlay assumed that the transmitter of the disease was the mosquito, and this was confirmed by Maj. Walter (Reed) in 1900 and proved by William Georges at the beginning of the twentieth century. By eliminating mosquitoes during the digging of the Panama Canal, the disease was reduced a great deal. During the same period, Patrick Manson discovered the filarial parasite that causes elephantiasis, and he found out that the transmitter thereof is the mosquito, which also transmits the malaria virus.

The word malaria is of Italian origin, meaning "bad air." This word is still used although it reflects the mistaken notion that the disease was transmitted to humans via bad air, which is what was thought before the role of the mosquito in transmitting the microscopic beings that cause it, was discovered. Hence, when the Qur'an tells us not to look down at the mosquito, this is indicative of its significance, and it also includes that which is even smaller than it. Thus the Qur'an was more than ten centuries ahead of the scientific era; it alone is the Word of Allah, the Exalted, that remains for all nations, especially since these scientific references are not found in any other record that is attributed to Divine Revelation.

One of the amazing things about the Qur'an's eloquence is that it chooses to refer to the mosquito in the feminine singular, instead of using the masculine or the plural which would include both genders. It is a well-known fact that it is the female mosquito alone that feeds on blood and transmits disease, and the male has no mouth parts that are capable of piercing the skin. Thus the Qur'an uses words and phrases that coincided with reality before 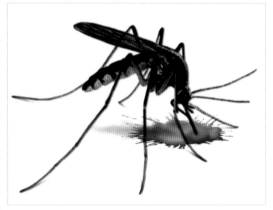 it was discovered. Saying that there is no shame in highlighting the significance of the mosquito and creatures like it implies that it is wrong to look down on it and also highlights ignorance of its significance at the time of revelation.

The fact that there are many types of mosquito is reflected in the usage of the word Ba'oodah (mosquito) in the indefinite form. Different species of mosquitoes and microscopic beings vary in their shapes and habits, and also in the specific weapons by means of which they challenge man and attack animals; one kind may cause many specific types of diseases to specific victims. This conflict with small creatures

is like a battle in which the soldiers are destined to defeat their enemies all the time. Thus it became an eternal challenge to man's arrogance and pride and a clear example of Allah's miraculous power and care for His creation, no matter how small. Thus the Qur'an challenges man with a tiny mosquito and that which is smaller than it; this is a sign of Allah's All-Encompassing knowledge and proof of the Divine nature of the Revelation. We can see how true it is and how strong is the evidence of the Divine knowledge of the secrets of creation in the words,

﴿ وَمَا يَعْلَمُ جُنُودَ رَبِّكَ إِلَّا هُوَ وَمَا هِىَ إِلَّا ذِكْرَىٰ لِلْبَشَرِ ﴾

"And none can know the hosts of your Lord but He. And this (Hell) is nothing else than a (warning) reminder to mankind." (Soorah Al-Muddaththir, 74:31)

If man realized in the true sense of the word that the mosquito and every atom in the universe glorifies and exalts Allah, and bears witness to His Power, Majesty and Might, and he filled his mind with this concept, that would distract him from eating, let alone idle deeds and words. There is no atom in creation that does not invite man's reason to understand Allah and His attributes. This mosquito alone, in the manner in which its essence and attributes are created, points to the power of Allah, Most High; its magnificent composition points to the Knowledge of Allah and the Will of Allah. It is as if He is saying: How could He feel ashamed to point to such a thing as this?

How can anybody not worship Allah, Alone, when this is the sign of His creation and power? How can anybody ascribe rivals to Allah, the Exalted, when His miracles so clearly exist in that which can be seen and that which cannot be seen?

Allah is the Lord of all things, great and small; He is the Creator of the mosquito and the elephant. The miracle of the mosquito is the same as that of the elephant; it is the miracle of life and the miracle of the locked secret that is known only to Allah. But what matters in parables is not size, rather parables are tools of enlightenment and insight. In using the mosquito as a parable there is nothing that could be a source of shame.

﴿ فَأَمَّا ٱلَّذِينَ ءَامَنُواْ فَيَعْلَمُونَ أَنَّهُ ٱلْحَقُّ مِن رَّبِّهِمْ ﴾

"And as for those who believe, they know that it is the Truth from their Lord." (Soorah Al-Baqarah, 2:26).

Their faith in Allah, the Almighty, causes them to receive everything that comes from Him in a manner that befits His Majesty and in a manner that befits their knowledge of His Wisdom. Their faith gives them light in their hearts and the ability to understand the connection with Divine wisdom in everything and in every statement that comes to them from Allah.

﴿ وَأَمَّا ٱلَّذِينَ كَفَرُواْ فَيَقُولُونَ مَاذَآ أَرَادَ ٱللَّهُ بِهَٰذَا مَثَلًا ﴾

"But as for those who disbelieve, they say: 'What did Allah intend by this parable'?" (Soorah Al-Baqarah, 2:26).

This is the question of the one who is deprived of the light of Allah, the Exalted, and His Knowledge, and who has no understanding of the way of Allah and His creation.

*****

Flies

It was narrated that Abu Hurairah, may Allah be pleased with him, said, the Prophet, peace and blessings of Allah be upon him, said:

"If a fly falls into the drink of one of you, let him submerge it and then remove it, for on one of its wings is a disease and on the other is healing." (Narrated by Al-Bukhari and Ahmad

This *Hadith* is one of the medical miracles of the Prophet, peace and blessings of Allah be upon him, which should be recorded by medical history in letters of gold, because it stated that the cause of disease and the cause of healing exist on the two wings of the fly, fourteen hundred years before this was discovered. It states that if a fly, on one of whose wings are germs that cause disease, falls into water, the way to purify the water is to submerge the fly so that the factors of healing that are present on the other wing will also enter the water, and will thus destroy the disease-causing germs. Modern scientific experiments have proved the mysterious secret behind this *Hadith*, which is that there is a specific characteristic in one of the fly's wings that moves the bacteria to one side. Based on this, if the fly falls onto food or drink, it sheds the bacteria that are attached to the edges of its wings onto the food or drink, and the closest destroyer of those germs is the destroyer of bacteria that is carried by the fly in its stomach near one of its wings. So if there is a disease, its remedy is close by. Hence, submerging the entire fly and then removing it is sufficient to kill the germs that were clinging to it, and is sufficient to cancel out their effect.

It has also been proved scientifically that the fly secretes small bodies of a type of enzyme called bacteriophage which destroys germs. This bacteriophage or healing factor is very small (20-25 nanometers long). If a fly falls into food or drink, it must be submerged so that these antibodies may be released and destroy the germs that were transmitted. Science has proved what the Prophet, peace and blessings of Allah be upon him, said in a miraculous manner, to those  who rejected the *Hadith*. Dr. Ameen Rida, a professor of orthopaedic surgery in the Faculty of Medicine at Alexandria University, conducted research on the narration of the fly in which he confirmed that all medical reference books contain prescriptions for various diseases using flies. In modern times, surgeons who lived in the ten years prior to the discovery of sulfa drugs, i.e. in the 1930s, stated that they saw with their own eyes cases where compound fractures and chronic ulcers were treated with flies.

Hence, it is clear that science in its developments has proved and confirmed what is mentioned in the narration, which is regarded as a scientific miracle of which the Prophet, peace and blessings of Allah be upon him, spoke long ago.

(Al-'Ijaz Al-'Ilmi Fil-Islam Was-Sunnah An-Nabawiyah)

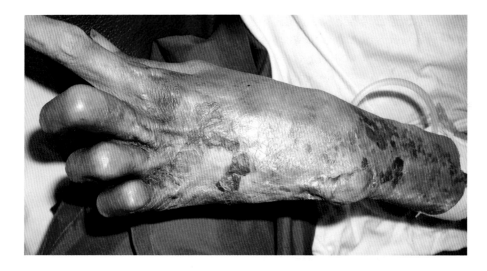

Leprosy

Modern science has proved that leprosy is one of the most serious skin diseases that is transmitted via infection with the leprosy bacteria which was finally seen and recognized more than a hundred years ago. However, modern science up till now is unable to control this disease. Leprosy affects the nerve endings such as those in the arms, and causes the patient to lose all sensation, so he does not feel pain or heat and cold, rather a thorn may be inserted in his foot without him feeling it. The patient also experiences atrophy in the muscles of the arms and legs, and lesions on the skin, especially on the feet and hands. The bones waste away and some parts may be lost, such as the fingers and toes. It may also affect the cornea of the eye, affecting the vision.

Leprosy may also affect the testicles, which means that the leper may lose sexual function and thus have no children.

Leprosy is of two types:

*   Lepromatous leprosy (multibacillary Hansen's disease): This affects the patient with a weak immune system and appears in the form of small knots or nodules of various sizes on the

body and especially in the face. It takes on a particular shape resembling the face of a lion. It also causes the hair of the eyebrows to fall out and may affect the mucous lining of the nose, causing nosebleeds.

- Tuberculoid leprosy (paucibacillary Hansen's disease) which affects the skin, leading to light spots of various shapes and sizes: These spots are affected by loss of feeling and sweating, and a reduction in the amount of melanin in the skin. This type of leprosy may affect people with relatively strong immune systems.

It is a sign of the greatness of the Prophet's teachings that he said to those whom Allah has blessed with good health and spared them from this dreadful disease: "Do not stare at lepers." (Al-Tayalisi and Al-Baihaqi, from Ibn 'Abbas; it is a *saheeh Hadith*)

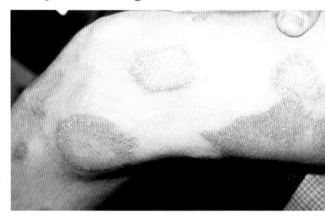

Modern psychology has proved that if the leper sees a healthy person staring at him, his sense of calamity becomes even greater and he feels very sorry for himself.

Hence, the prohibition on staring at them is out of consideration for their feelings. The Prophet, peace and blessings of Allah be upon him, understood how contagious the leper is, so he ordered healthy people to keep away from him immediately, just as a person would keep away from a ravaging lion, especially since the leprosy bacteria will devor a healthy person if it is transmitted to him. This narration was spoken more than fourteen hundred years ago, and modern science has proved its validity and offered the same advice as the Prophet, peace and blessings of Allah be upon him, gave.

(*Al-'Ijaz Al-'Ilmi Fil-Qur'an*)

Flee from the Leper

It was narrated that Abu Hurairah, may Allah be pleased with him, said: The Messenger of Allah, peace and blessings of Allah be upon him, said: "There is no *'Adwa* (contagion, transmission of infectious disease without the permission of Allah), no *Tiyarah* (superstitious belief in bird omens), no *Hammah* (refers to a Jahili Arab tradition described variously as: a worm which infests the grave of a murder victim until he is avenged; an owl; or the bones of a dead person turned into a bird that could fly), and no *Safar* (the month of Safar was regarded as "unlucky" during the *Jahiliyah*), but flee from the leper as you would flee from a lion." (Narrated by Ahmad and by Al-Bukhari in a *Mu'allaq* report)

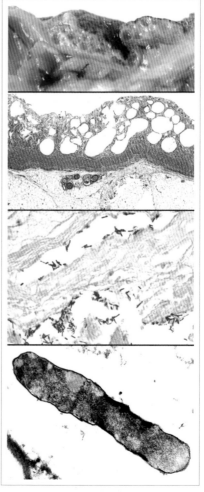

Rod-shaped bacterium

The scholars have reconciled the words, "flee from the leper as you would flee from a lion," with the words, "There is no *'Adwa* (contagion)" in many ways. Some of them thought that the command to keep away from the leper is to be interpreted as meaning that one should take no chances and should block the means, lest mixing with him leads to any illness; it was thought that the cause of disease was mixing, thus confirming the contagion that was denied by the Lawgiver. This is supported by what was narrated by Al-Tirmidhi from Jabir, may Allah be pleased with him, who said, The Prophet, peace and blessings of Allah be upon him, took the hand of a leper and put it in the plate, and said: "Eat, putting your trust in Allah and

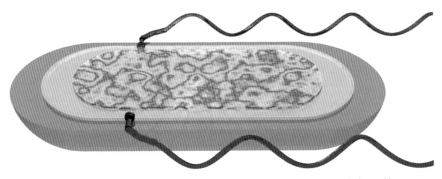

Rod-shaped bacterium

depending on Him."

The Prophet, peace and blessings of Allah be upon him, ate with a leper to show them that Allah is the One Who causes sickness and grants healing, but he forbade them to come close to a leper in order to show them that this is one of the means which Allah, the Almighty, has dictated should lead to certain ends. It is possible that his eating with the leper was a brief interaction which does not lead to infection with this disease, because not all lepers are the same and contagion does not occur in all cases. It has been proved scientifically that the rate of infection with this disease is very low, as more than 90 percent of people have a natural immunity against it. It is a disease that affects the skin, nerves, eyes, testicles, bones, upper respiratory system and other parts of the body. This disease is caused by a rod-shaped bacterium that is transmitted from a sick person to a healthy one by respiratory means, skin-to-skin contact or by bites from certain insects. The ten percent of people who have no natural immunity to this disease may be divided into two categories:

- Those whose immunity is weak; in this case the disease takes hold.
- Those who have almost no immunity.

The low rate of infection explains to us the reason why the Prophet, peace and blessings of Allah be upon him, ate with the leper.

(See *Haqa'iq Al-Tibbiyah Fil-Islam*)

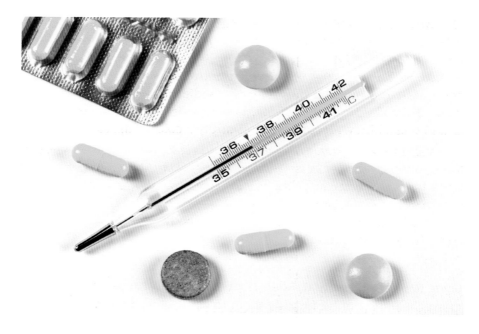

Fever and Remedies

A person's body temperature may rise for a number of reasons, including bacterial or viral infection. If the temperature rises to 41 degrees Celsius, it must be brought down quickly, so that the temperature center in the brain will go back to normal and the body will return to its usual state. This sudden rise in temperature is known as a fever. The Prophet, peace and blessings of Allah be upon him, prescribed in a number of narrations a remedy for reducing a high temperature.

He called for using cold water to extinguish the fire of fever which is raging in the body of the sick person. Imams Al-Bukhari and Muslim narrated from 'A'ishah, may Allah be pleased with her, that the Prophet, peace and blessings of Allah be upon him, said: "Fever is a breeze from Hell, so cool it down with water." And when his fever grew intense during his final illness, he ordered that seven full skins of water be emptied over him. (Narrated by Al-Bukhari)

Although there have been leaps and bounds in the development of remedies and antibiotics in modern times, the Prophet's remedy remains the most beneficial and best in such cases. In many cases where there is a high temperature, anti-fever medicines do not work, so doctors have to use cold water to reduce the fever and bring the body back to its normal state. Hence, paediatricians advise families to take off the child's clothes straight away when his temperature rises, and to wash him with cold water or apply a cold compress.

It has also been proved scientifically and confirmed in the *Sunnah*, that the fever which affects a person has a number of benefits. It has been proved that when the sick person gets a fever, the levels of interferon increase. This is a substance that is produced by white blood cells, and is able to kill off the viruses that attacked the body and is more able to produce antibodies. It does not only rid the body of viruses and bacteria, but it increases the body's resistance to disease and helps to kill off cancer cells when they first appear, thus protecting the body from the emergence of any cancer cells that may lead to developing cancer. Some doctors say that fever is often a good sign as it heralds recovery, and fever may be more beneficial than taking medicine, as in the case of rheumatism in which the joints become stiff and unable to move. One of the remedies that are used in such cases is inducing fever artificially, by injecting the patient with a certain substance.

Hence, when fever was mentioned in the presence of the Messenger of Allah, peace and blessings of Allah be upon him, and a man cursed it, the Prophet, peace and blessings of Allah be upon him, said to him: "Do not curse it, for it erases sin as the fire erases the dross of iron." (Narrated by Ahmad)

May the blessings and peace of Allah be upon the Prophet of Mercy who diagnosed the disease and also prescribed its remedy.

*****

Obesity

Ahmad, Al-Tirmidhi and Ibn Majah narrated that Al-Miqdam Ibn Ma'di Yakrib Al-Kindi said, I heard the Messenger of Allah, peace and blessings of Allah be upon him, say: "The son of Adam does not fill any vessel worse than his stomach. It is sufficient for the son of Adam to eat a few mouthfuls, to keep him going. If he must do that (fill his stomach), then let him fill one third with food, one third with drink and one third with air…" (*Saheeh*)

Science has found out that from a health point of view, obesity is regarded as a defect in assimilation of food; that is due to an accumulation of fat or a disorder in the endocrine glands. Hereditary factors do not play a major role in obesity as some believe. Scientific research has confirmed that being overweight has negative consequences for the human body. An American insurance company has issued statistics showing that the greater a person's waist circumference the lower his life expectancy, so men whose waist measurements exceed their chest measurements die in relatively larger numbers.

Research has also proved that diabetes affects those who are overweight more than average, as being overweight affects the faculties, especially the heart, as fat takes the place of some of the muscle cells in the heart, which directly affects its function. In this narration the Prophet, peace and blessings of Allah be upon him, warned against being overweight and overeating. And Allah, the Exalted, says:

﴿ وَكُلُوا۟ وَٱشۡرَبُوا۟ وَلَا تُسۡرِفُوٓا۟ إِنَّهُۥ لَا يُحِبُّ ٱلۡمُسۡرِفِينَ ﴾

"And eat and drink but waste not by extravagance, certainly He (Allah) likes not Musrifoon (those who waste by extravagance)." (Soorah Al-A'raf, 7:31)

This research warns against using drugs to reduce weight because of the harm they cause, and it indicates that the best remedy for overweight and the best way to protect oneself against it is to follow that which Allah has enjoined, of avoiding extravagance in eating, and to follow the *Sunnah* of the Messenger of Allah, peace and blessings of Allah be upon him, in eating as described in the narration under discussion.

In recent times a new operation has recently been introduced for severely overweight people to reduce their weight, in which the doctor ties the stomach, isolating the top third temporarily so that the stomach cannot be filled. If food enters the stomach, it fills the upper third only, until the patient's appetite is

reduced and he gets used to eating less, and his weight is reduced by half or more in a few months. I have seen some of them before and after this surgery in a program on satellite TV.

Thus, more than fourteen hundred years ago, Islam was the first to point out the importance of moderation in consuming food and drink, and warned of the dangers of extravagance to human health.

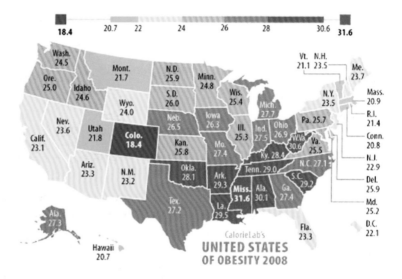

CalorieLab's
**UNITED STATES
OF OBESITY 2008**

Obesity threatens a large number of Americans

Julie Gerberding, the director of the Centers for Disease Control and Prevention in the USA, said on 11 July 2003 that obesity will soon become the primary cause of death in the country, and she warned that it has begun to threaten the health of a large number of Americans. It has now reached a rate of 28 percent in America. Gerberding called for making this problem a priority of health care systems nationwide, and suggested that ways of preventing obesity be set up. She pointed out that simple changes such as using the stairs instead of the elevator and reducing one's intake of calories by 100 calories per day could play a role in combating obesity.

Being overweight increases risk of heart failure

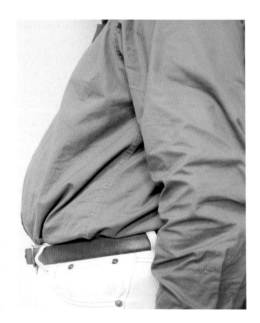

A recent American study shows that increased weight increases the risk of heart failure.

The study, which was published in the *New England Journal of Medicine*, indicates that the risk of heart failure in overweight women is more than double, and is slightly less in the case of overweight men.

This study is the latest in a long series of research which shows that being overweight is a serious matter, which may cause death. The doctors who carried out the study said: The research is important because of the increasing number of people who suffer from excess weight in the United States.

The study concluded that even a small increase in weight may pose a risk. The research team discovered that every increase of one point in the body-mass index (BMI) leads to an increased risk of heart failure, at a rate of 5 percent for men and 7 percent for women.

The researchers said that previous studies showed that obesity increases the risk of heart failure but they did not show precisely the effect of a small increase in weight. (A Reuters report)

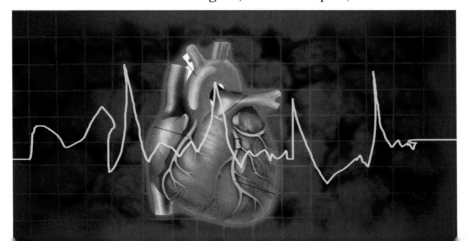

Canadian experts: Obesity affects mental health

Obesity and excess weight do not only affect physical health; they also affect mental health. This is what was discovered by researchers at the University of Toronto in Canada.

While many studies have made the connection between obesity and serious cardiovascular diseases, including heart failure and heart attacks, the Toronto researchers discovered that overeating may also destroy a person's general state of health, by slowing down his thought processes and reflexes.

Dr. Costas Tarakes, a researcher in pharmacology at the University of Toronto, says that obesity has a daily impact on every aspect of life, and it harms the mind as it harms the body.

The Canadian study, which was published in the International Journal of Obesity, used Canadian health statistics to analyze different aspects of life for Canadians from 1996 to 1997, taking into consideration gender, weight, smoking habits, level of education, income and other factors connected to weight gain.

The researchers noticed that individuals who were obese or overweight recorded slower levels of thinking and higher levels of pain and limited movement, in addition to other problems. They indicated that one in every seven Canadians is obese, and women are affected more.

(Source: *Quds Press*)

Obesity threatens the achievements of modern medicine

British nutrition specialists said on 12 July 2003: Obesity threatens the increase in average lifespan that was achieved during the last century, and may lead in some cases to parents living longer than their children.

The number of people affected by obesity in the United States is estimated at 28 percent and at 20 percent in Europe. There are also a large number of people who are overweight, which makes obesity the fastest spreading health problem in the last two decades.

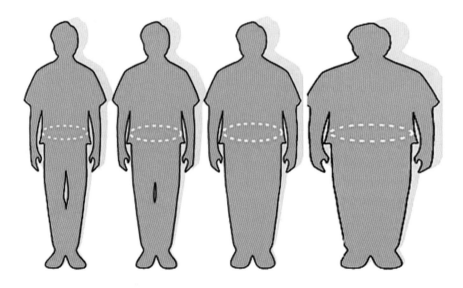

A researcher in the London School of Hygiene and Tropical Medicine, Andrew Prentice, states that the epidemic results from eating too much fat and not getting enough physical exercise, two things which have an impact on human development.

But contrary to the changes that occurred two centuries ago as the result of improved nourishment, which led to increases in height, humans now are starting to become obese at an early age.

Prentice says concerning obesity and smoking, "We spent one

hundred years doing a marvellous job in increasing man's lifespan and improving his health, but now there are a few things that threaten us."

He added, "Overweight is largely to blame, and it is possible that it may lead to the opposite of all the achievements we have made. The weight of adolescents is continually increasing, and doctors have noticed an increase in the number of people affected by diabetes resulting from obesity in younger patients."

Prentice adds that there are cases in which parents outlive their children, who die as the result of obesity. The researcher believes that the problem is compounded because fat children are likely to remain fat when they reach adolescence, and the earlier obesity occurs, the greater effect it has on health. (A Reuters report)

Protecting the digestive system

In a *Hadith* narrated by Al-Suyooti in *Al-Jami' As-Sagheer*, the Prophet, peace and blessings of Allah be upon him, said, "The source of all sickness is indigestion caused by overeating." (Narrated by Al-Daraqutni in *Al-'Ilal* from Anas, and by Ibn Al-Sunni and Abu Na'eem in *Al-Tibb* from 'Ali and Abu Sa'eed; narrated by Al-Zuhri in a *mursal* report. It is a very weak *Hadith* (*Dha'eef Jiddan*). See: *Kashf Al-Khifa'*, 380

Although this *Hadith* is not *saheeh* or *marfoo'*, its meaning represents a prominent landmark in protecting the health of the digestive system, and thus protecting the body as a whole from self-poisoning which results

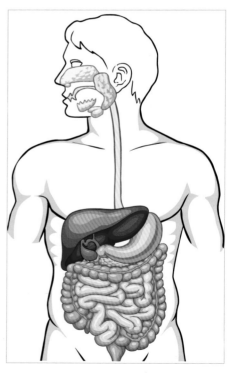

digestive system

from overeating and filling the stomach and burdening it with more than it can bear of heavy food, and from eating again before the first food has been digested, which causes indigestion, and, hence, severe stomach infections which may become chronic as a result of germs residing in the intestine, which send toxins to the circulatory system, then they affect the nervous, respiratory, renal and urinary systems, and other vital systems in the body, which causes disruption of bodily functions.

Thus the medical miracle lies in the possibility of arriving at the basic cause of all disease, which is extravagance in consuming food, which causes indigestion, which in turn leads to numerous diseases as has been discovered by modern scientific research.

Digestion of food

The *Hadith* quoted above contains a number of scientific facts, including,

- The harm that results from eating too much food.
- The effect that filling the stomach with food has on one's breathing; a person may experience difficulty in breathing if he fills his stomach with food.
- The benefits of drinking water with food.

In the book *Al-Sunnah Al-Mutahharah Wal-Tahaddiyat*, the author tells of a colleague of his, who was a senior lecturer in the medical school of the University of Damascus. He said to him, "How can we accept the words of these foreigners and not accept the words of the Prophet, peace and blessings of Allah be upon him?" Then he told a story from his scientific career which offers a lesson to everyone who thinks and ponders. He said: When I was first appointed as a teacher in medical school, I always told people of the health benefit to the healthy body of drinking water with food, based on the *saheeh Hadith*: "One-third for his food, one-third for his drink and one-third for his air."

I noticed the beneficial effect of that in myself and my patients whose number now has reached half a million. At that time the students held the contrary view, because in the books that they had before them, which were taken from foreigners, they found the opposite view. But I insisted on my opinion and went against those books.

More recently, medical science also began to confirm what is mentioned in the *saheeh Hadith,* and began to recommend drinking water with food, because doctors realized that drinking water with food helps to increase secretion of digestive juices in the stomach, liver and intestine, and it helps the digestive system function by softening the food and making it like dough, so that the digestive juices may penetrate it; this also helps to prevent constipation. I used to recommend patients with chronic constipation to drink a lot of water with their food.

When the Prophet, peace and blessings of Allah be upon him, allocated the last third for air, he did not discuss scientific facts that only became known in the twentieth century, when Pavlov studied digestive secretions in dogs, when he opened a dog's stomach and studied how it digested food and produced digestive juices. The Prophet, peace and blessings of Allah be upon him, did not discuss what happens in the stomach; he only mentioned leaving one-third for air because food requires digestion, and digestion cannot be done without the digestive secretions, but if the stomach is filled with food, where can room be found for the digestive juices?

There is another secret in this *Hadith.* Scientists in the US have invented a new way to reduce weight, by inserting balloons into the stomach and inflating them until they fill one-third of the stomach, leaving the other two-thirds of the stomach empty for food. Researchers have discovered that this is an effective means of reducing weight. Is this not what was taught by the Messenger, peace and blessings of Allah be upon him, more than fourteen hundred years ago?

(Qabasat Min Al-Tibb An-Nabawi, Al-Adillah Al-'Ilmiyah Al-Hadithah; Al-Sunnah Al-Mutahharah Wal-Tahaddiyat)

*****

Anger and Emotion

Allah, the Exalted, has instilled in man a number of instincts and feelings; he is affected by what happens around him and he interacts with what he sees and hears from others. He laughs and cries, is happy and sad, feels content and gets angry, and experiences other emotions.

One of the things that the Messenger of Allah, peace and blessings of Allah be upon him, forbade was giving free rein to anger, because it may cause a person to lose control and may lead to negative consequences. In his *Saheeh*, Al-Bukhari narrated from Abu Hurairah, may Allah be pleased with him, that a man said to the Prophet, peace and blessings of Allah be upon him, "Advise me." He said: "Do not get angry."

He repeated his question several times, and the Prophet answered in the same manner: "Do not get angry."

However, the Prophet, peace and blessings of Allah be upon him, did not stop at forbidding this attitude and explaining the means that lead to it, rather he explained the means and remedies that a person may use to reduce the severity of his anger and avoid its consequences. One of these means is keeping quiet and not talking too much.

In the narration, the Prophet, peace and blessings of Allah be upon him, said: "If you get angry, then sit down." (*Al-Khara'iti fi Masawi' Al-Akhlaq*, from 'Imran Ibn Husain. *Saheeh*)

Imam Ahmad, may Allah have Mercy upon him, narrated that Ibn 'Abbas, may Allah be pleased with him, said, The Messenger of Allah, peace and blessings of Allah be upon him, said: "Teach and make things easy, do not make things hard. If you get angry then keep quiet; if you get angry then keep quiet; if you get angry then keep quiet."

Ahmad, may Allah have Mercy upon him, and Al-Tirmidhi, may Allah have Mercy upon him, narrated that the Prophet, peace and blessings of Allah be upon him, said: "Anger is a coal that is lit in the heart of man. Do you not see the redness of his eyes and the swelling of his cheeks? If one of you experiences anything of that, let him sit on the ground, on the ground. The best of men is the one who is slow to anger and quick to be pleased, and the worst of men is the one who is quick to anger and slow to be pleased." (There is some weakness in it, but it has corroborating reports that strengthen it.)

Another means of reducing anger is by performing *Wudhoo'* (ablution).

It was narrated that 'Atiyah Al-Sa'di, may Allah have Mercy on him,

Adrenal gland

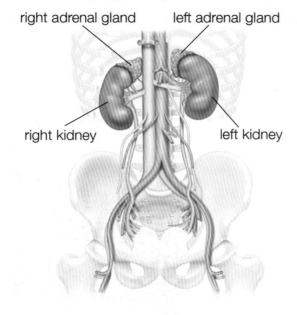

right adrenal gland

left adrenal gland

right kidney

left kidney

said, The Messenger of Allah, peace and blessings of Allah be upon him, said: "Anger comes from the *Shaitan,* and the *Shaitan* was created from fire, and fire is extinguished by water, so if one of you gets angry, let him do *Wudhoo'*." (Narrated by Ahmad and Abu Dawood. There is some weakness in it, but it was classed as *hasan* by some of the scholars.)

One of the important remedies that the Prophet, peace and blessings of Allah be upon him, taught for dealing with anger and reducing its severity, which has been confirmed by modern medicine, is to change the posture one is in when anger strikes, from standing to sitting or lying down.

It was narrated from Abu Dharr, may Allah be pleased with him, that the Prophet, peace and blessings of Allah be upon him, said: "If one of you gets angry and he is standing, let him sit down, and if the anger goes away, all well and good, otherwise let him lie down." (Narrated by Ahmad and Abu Dawood: *Saheeh.*)

Modern medicine has discovered that there are a number of changes in the human body that are caused by anger. The adrenal gland, which is located above the kidney, secretes two kinds of hormones, adrenaline and noradrenaline. Adrenaline is secreted in response to any kind of emotion or psychological pressure, such as fear or anger; it may also be secreted due to lack of sugar. These two hormones are usually secreted together.

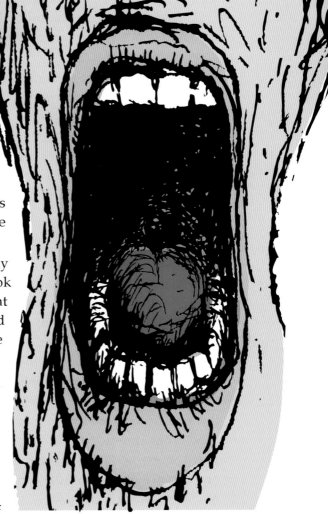

The secretion of this hormone affects the heart beat, which becomes irregular and rapid; the heart muscles contract and consume more oxygen. Anger and other emotions lead to a rise in the level of these two hormones in the blood, which in turn leads to an increased heartbeat and may also lead to a rise in blood pressure. Hence, doctors advise patients who have high blood pressure or narrowing of the arteries to avoid becoming emotional or angry, and to keep away from things that cause that. They advise diabetics similarly because adrenaline increases blood sugar too.

It has been proved scientifically – as it says in Harrison's book of medicine – that the amount of noradrenaline in the blood increases as much as two or three fold when standing quietly for five minutes, and the amount of adrenaline rises slightly when standing, but psychological pressure and emotion leads to a large increase in the level of adrenaline in the blood. If a person stands quietly for five minutes, the amount of noradrenaline increases, but if he is angry and emotional, the level of adrenaline in the blood increases greatly. Imagine what would happen if the two things, anger and standing, come together? Hence, the Prophet, peace and blessings of

Allah be upon him, advised the angry person who is standing to sit down, and if that does not take away his anger, to lie down.

Another remedy that the Prophet, peace and blessings of Allah be upon him, taught for dealing with anger and reducing its severity is to seek refuge with Allah, the Exalted, from the accursed *Shaitan*, i.e., if a person gets angry, he should seek refuge with Allah and ask Him to help him deal with this anger that has been caused by the accursed *Shaitan*.

It was narrated that Sulaiman Ibn Surad, may Allah be pleased with him, said, I was sitting with the Prophet, peace and blessings of Allah be upon him, and there were two men trading insults. One of them was red in the face and his veins were standing out. The Prophet, peace and blessings of Allah be upon him, said: "I know a word which, if he says it, what he is feeling would go away. If he says *'A'oodhu Billahi Min As-Shaitan ir-Rajeem* (I seek refuge with Allah from the accursed *Shaitan*)' what he is feeling would go away." They told him that the Prophet, peace and blessings of Allah be upon him, had said: "Seek refuge with Allah from the *Shaitan*" and he said, "Am I insane?" (Agreed upon)

It was narrated from Abu Hurairah, may Allah be pleased with him, that the Prophet, peace and blessings of Allah be upon him, said: "If a man gets angry and says *A'oodhu Billah* (I seek refuge with Allah), his anger will subside." (Ibn 'Adiyy: *Saheeh*)

Ibn Al-Sunni, may Allah have Mercy upon him, narrated from 'A'ishah, may Allah be pleased with her, that if she got angry, the Prophet, peace and blessings of Allah be upon him, would tweak her nose and say: "O 'Uwaysh, say: 'O Allah, Lord of Muhammad, forgive me my sin and take away the resentment from my heart, and protect me from misleading turmoil'." (There is some weakness in it.)

This prior knowledge of the Prophet, peace and blessings of Allah be upon him, was one of the miracles that did not become apparent until modern times. Otherwise, how could he have known that these hormones increase when one is standing and decrease when one sits down or lies down, in order to prescribe this prophetic remedy to us? May the blessings and peace of Allah, Most High, be upon him and all the Prophets and Messengers.

Summary

It has been proved scientifically that anger, like other emotions, affects the heart in the same manner as running and jogging. Anger increases the number of times that the muscles contract per minute, which in turn increases the amount of blood pumped by the heart to the blood vessels with every heartbeat. This exhausts the heart because it forces it to work harder than what it is usually supposed to do under ordinary circumstances. In the case of running or jogging, the increased heart rate does not last for long, because a person can stop jogging when he wants to, but in the case of anger he cannot control his anger, especially if he is not used to controlling his feelings. It has been noted that an individual who is habitually angry will have higher than normal blood pressure, because his heart is compelled to push a higher than average amount of blood. The walls of the narrow veins become harder and lose their flexibility and ability to expand in order to allow the increased volume of blood pumped by the emotion-affected heart to pass. Hence, his blood pressure rises when he becomes angry.

It is worth noting that in the past, scholars believed that anger which was expressed was not harmful, and that it was only suppressed anger that was responsible for many diseases. But a recent American study offered a new explanation for the effect of both kinds of anger. In brief, suppressing or expressing anger both cause the same damage to health, although the severity of the damage may differ. Suppressed anger, if it occurs repeatedly, leads to a rise in blood pressure and sometimes to cancer. If the anger is expressed repeatedly, that may lead to damage of

the coronary arteries and the possibility of a fatal heart attack, because the explosion of anger may increase its severity and make it difficult to control anger, no matter how little it is.

The individual's physical state cannot be separated from his psychological state. His psychological condition may lead to his glands producing more of their secretions, thus affecting the immune system and preventing the antibodies that are produced by this system from reaching their goals.

More serious than all of that is the fact that some of the most effective weapons used by the body to defend itself, which are released by some of the glands, may become very weak as the result of this gland contracting as the result of a serious psychological problem. This explains the reason why healthy cells may turn to cancerous ones in the absence of the immune system's natural activity. The Messenger of Allah, peace and blessings of Allah be upon him, spoke the truth when he advised us not to get angry. Hence we can see the scientific and practical wisdom in repeated counsel of the Prophet, peace and blessings of Allah be upon him, to that questioner not to get angry.

*****

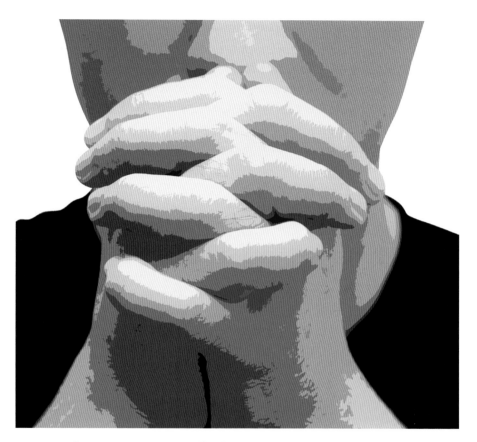

The Powerful Healing Effect of Forgiveness and Tolerance

Italian researchers have produced scientific evidence to support the idea of the benefit of forgiveness and tolerance, not only because this is required from a moral point of view, as religion says, but also because forgiveness is beneficial to health. Professor Bino Bitrini, a neurologist at the University of Pisa in Italy, tested the soundness of the idea that forgiveness allows a person to overcome a situation which could become a major source of depression that could affect the mind and nerves, were it not for forgiveness.

The professor received sponsorship for this study from a nonprofit

organization called the Campaign for Research on Tolerance.

In this study, he presented topics for each of which he offered two scenarios, one of tolerance and the other of non-tolerance, in order to create a certain emotional state and then he observed the effects thereof on brain activity by using modern equipment that measures brain function.

Professor Bitrini told the German news agency DPA that he wanted to test the assumption that tolerance and forgiveness lead to better health. He gave the example of a woman who was unable to forgive her husband for his betrayal.

Bitrini said that divorce leads to a high rate of depression and may cause a person to become mentally unbalanced. The easiest way to avoid the negative effects on the mind and body is to forgive. Research has been done in the United States which supports this idea.

A group of researchers at the University of Wisconsin carried out an experiment on 46 male subjects who were affected by coronary artery disease, whose lives include stories of war, bad memories of childhood, family problems or disputes in the workplace.

They concluded that for those who received training in forgiveness and tolerance, the flow of blood to the heart improved.

The idea of forgiving and overlooking mistakes is prevalent in religions of heavenly origin.

Christianity calls its followers to follow the example of the Messiah, who called for compassion and put it into practice. Judaism and Islam call for overlooking the mistakes, which cause pain and forsaking anger which is accompanied by a desire for revenge.

In the Qur'an there are many Verses which encourage people to forgive the mistakes of those who mistreat them. Allah says:

$$﴿ فَٱصْفَحِ ٱلصَّفْحَ ٱلْجَمِيلَ ﴾$$

"So overlook, (O Muhammad), their faults with gracious forgiveness." (Soorah Al-Hijr, 15:85)

$$﴿ وَعِبَادُ ٱلرَّحْمَٰنِ ٱلَّذِينَ يَمْشُونَ عَلَى ٱلْأَرْضِ هَوْنًا وَإِذَا خَاطَبَهُمُ ٱلْجَٰهِلُونَ قَالُوا سَلَٰمًا ﴾$$

"And the (faithful) slaves of the Most Gracious (Allah) are those who walk on the earth in humility and sedateness, and when the foolish address them (with bad words) they reply back with mild words of gentleness." (Soorah Al-Furqan, 25:63]

Similarly, in the *Sunnah* of the Prophet , peace and blessings of Allah be upon him, there are narrations which encourage overlooking mistreatment and casting aside resentment and grudges. Ibn Al-Najjar, may Allah have Mercy upon him, narrated with a *saheeh isnad* from the Prophet, peace and blessings of Allah be upon him, that he said: "Uphold ties with the one who cuts you off, treat kindly the one who mistreats you, and speak the truth even if it is against yourself."

In the varied heritage of humanity there is a great deal of praise for the attitude of tolerance and forgiveness among people. For a long time I thought that the motive for that was simply to put an end to disputes and hatred among people and to spread peace and love among all people in society.

But recently I read that there is a special benefit of forgiveness

that may reach the one who has been mistreated when he forgives this mistreatment.

Psychological research states that bearing grudges and resentment leads to misery and contributes to the development of physical disease in the body. Forgiving and forgetting bad treatment is regarded as a successful psychological approach that can put an end to painful symptoms caused by resentment and hatred in the heart.

The psychologist, Richard Fitzgibbons, says that during his twenty years of work he was able to study cases of extreme anger in different groups of people, male and female, adults, adolescents and children, and he was able to treat some of them whose mistreatment at the hands of others had generated in them feelings of anger, enmity and hatred and the desire for revenge. This was achieved by applying a strategy of forgiveness towards those who had mistreated them.

Dr. Fitzgibbons said that the advantage of forgiveness is that it enables the person who has been subjected to mistreatment to live in peace with himself. Feelings of resentment and anger spoil life and cause tension, anxiety and deep mental anguish, but forgiveness erases all of that. Forgiving one who mistreats you does not necessarily mean continuing the relationship with him or retaining one's former friendly feelings towards him, if there was any friendship earlier. Rather it simply means forgetting the mistreatment and erasing it from one's memory and thus erasing from the heart the anguish that it had generated.

But if a person is unable to forgive and forget, and also unable to take his rights from the one who wronged him, then the result may be the exact opposite. What is meant by suppressing anger and forgiving in the narration is forgiving when one is able to take revenge. The authors of *Al-Sunan* narrated with a *hasan isnad* from the Prophet, peace and blessings of Allah be upon him, that he said: "The one who is able to suppress his anger when he is able to act upon it, Allah will call him before all of creation and give him his choice of *Al-Hoor Al-'Ain*, and he will marry whomever among them he wants."

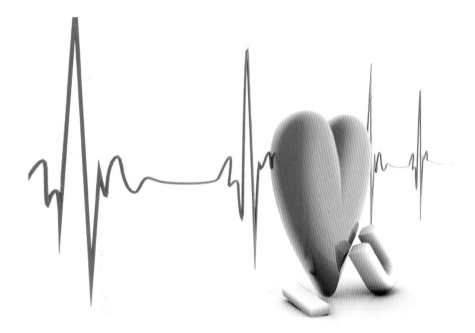

Anger and its negative effects

Dr. Ahmad Shawqi Ibrahim, a member of the Royal College of Physicians in London, and a consultant in internal and cardiac medicine, says: Human inclinations and feelings may be divided into three categories, and people's behavior and attitude differ depending on these inclinations and feelings and the extent to which one can control them.

- Physical inclinations which lead to revolt and anger
- Inclinations toward dominance, which lead to arrogance and love of leadership
- Devilish inclinations which cause hatred and resentment toward others

No matter what a person's inclinations, he is going to be exposed to anger and his body will react to that, so his blood pressure will rise and he will be affected by psychological and physical illnesses such as diabetes and angina. Scientific research has confirmed that getting angry repeatedly shortens a person's lifespan.

Hence, the Prophet, peace and blessings of Allah be upon him, advised the Muslims in his narration: "Do not get angry."

This does not mean that one should not get angry at all, rather it means that one should not get carried away with one's anger. A person should get angry if the sacred limits of Allah, the Exalted, are transgressed. The Messenger of Allah,

peace and blessings of Allah be upon him, said to one who got angry: "If one of you gets angry, let him keep quiet."

Since the angry person may do things that he would not approve of when his anger subsides, hence the Messenger, peace and blessings of Allah be upon him, said: "Let not one of you pass judgment between two people when he is angry." (Narrated by Muslim)

The Holy Qur'an depicts anger as a devilish force that overpowers man and pushes him to do things that he would not do if he were not angry. Prophet Moosa, peace be upon him, threw down the Tablets and seized his brother by the head and pulled him towards him. When his anger abated, he picked up the Tablets.

Allah, the Almighty, says:

﴿ وَلَمَّا سَكَتَ عَن مُّوسَى ٱلْغَضَبُ أَخَذَ ٱلْأَلْوَاحَ ﴾

"And when the anger of Moosa was calmed down, he took up the Tablets..." (Al-A'raf, 7:154)

It is as if anger is a kind of overpowering whisper of Satan (*Waswas*) that affected Moosa's thinking and caused him to throw down the

Tablets.

Avoiding anger requires self-control and strong faith in Allah, Most High. The Messenger, peace and blessings of Allah be upon him, praises these attributes in his narration when he says: "The strong man is not the one who can wrestle (fight); the strong man is the one who controls himself at the time of anger."

Avoiding anger is not done by taking tranquilizers, because they are only effective if taken regularly, and the one who takes tranquilizers cannot give them up easily. Anger changes one's behavior, so the remedy involves changing one's behavior and how one deals with daily problems; thus anger will turn into calmness and dignity.

Dr. Ahmad Shawqi adds: Psychology has reached two ways of treating the angry patient. One is by reducing his sensitivity, which involves training the patient, under the supervision of a doctor, to practice relaxation techniques while facing some difficult situation, so that he learns how to face situations without anger or emotion.

The other involves relaxing the mind and the muscles; the doctor asks the patient to remember difficult situations, and if he is standing then he should sit down or lie down, to give him the opportunity to think and relax. This remedy was only discovered recently by doctors, whereas the Prophet, peace and blessings of Allah be upon him, taught it to his companions in his narration: "If one of you gets angry and he is standing, let him sit down, and if his anger abates (all well and good), otherwise let him lie down." (Narrated by Ahmad and Abu Dawood; *Saheeh*)

(*Majallat Al-Islah*, issue No. 296, 1994, from *Nadawat Jama'iyah Al-'Ijaz Al-'Ilmi Fil-Qur'an* in Cairo)

*****

Bee Venom as a Remedy

The use of bee stings and bee venom dates back to Greek and Roman times, when people praised greatly the health benefits of bee venom and honey. Positive reviews regarding this natural product have continued until today, and have increased with research. Different ways have been developed of using it to treat inflammation of the joints and relapsing diseases, including various kinds of sclerosis of the nervous system. Scientific literature available on this topic includes more than 1500 articles and research papers.

Bee venom includes more than 18 active substances, the most important of which is melittin, which has an anti-inflammatory effect 100 times stronger than hydrocortisone, which is used to treat cases of inflammation that occur in the body. The venom also contains adolapin which acts as an anti-inflammatory and analgesic; and apamin which aids neurotransmission; and other substances, most of which are proteins which resist infection and soothe the tissues. Bee venom also contains a limited amount of chemical substances which play a role in neurotransmission, among the most important of which are dopamine, serotonin and epinephrine.

Many studies and reports have confirmed the importance of bee venom in treating rheumatism and other inflammations of the bones and joints, and relieving the pain caused by these conditions, as well as diseases of the connective tissues such as scleroderma and other diseases that have no connection to the joints, such as asthma and ulcerative colitis, slow-healing wounds, inflammation of the navel, tendonitis and other problems that require anti-inflammatory treatment and medication.

Bee venom is also beneficial in the treatment of scars, flattening them and reducing their colour.

Finally, interest has grown in the use of bee venom as a treatment for multiple sclerosis in the USA and among millions more in other regions of the world, because there is no cure for this disease. Many patients have tried to resort to alternative medicine to help them to control the different symptoms of this disease such as exhaustion, weakness, vision problems, loss of balance and loss of the ability to coordinate muscle movements, in addition to difficulty in walking and moving and deterioration in the ability to speak clearly, along with tremors and the possibility of partial or total paralysis in the worst cases.

Despite the lack of data or medical evidence confirming the soundness or effectiveness of bee venom as a treatment for multiple sclerosis, the American Multiple Sclerosis Society is sponsoring an important study to collect bee venom in bottles and inject it beneath the skin of patients who are taking part in this study, taking into account the fact that some patients may have a severe allergic reaction to bee

venom. For this reason, each participant in the study is subjected to a test to establish whether he has any allergy to bee venom. If the results show that he may react negatively to injection of bee venom, then the doctors in charge of the study refuse to allow him to take part. From the initial results it seems that a significant number of the participants experienced improved balance and their symptoms of exhaustion and tremors were reduced.

But the head of the American Multiple Sclerosis Society warned of the seriousness of the allergic reaction in some patients to bee venom, and recommended that it should not be used as a remedy for this sickness or any other health problems.

He also confirmed that this committee's sponsorship of this study was aimed only at finding out the nature of the possible benefits to the nervous system. If the results were positive, they would sponsor further studies and research, and encourage application of this remedy. But if the results were negative, they would have proved that the widespread claims about the efficacy of bee venom were false. And Allah, the Exalted, knows best.

* * * * *

Camel's Urine

It was narrated that Anas, may Allah be pleased with him, said: "Some people from 'Ukl came to the Prophet, peace and blessings of Allah be upon him, and became Muslim, but the climate of Madinah did not suit them. He told them to go to the Zakah camels and drink their milk and urine. They did that and became well, then they apostatized and killed the herdsmen and drove off the camels. He sent men after them. They were brought, and he had their hands and feet cut off and did not cauterize them, and their eyes put out, and he left them in the Harrah until they died." (Narrated by Al-Bukhari and Muslim)

Commentary on the *Hadith*

"The climate did not suit them" i.e., they did not want to stay there because of a sickness that befell them. According to another report, their stomachs swelled up and they turned yellow. "Their eyes (were) put out," it was narrated that Anas, may Allah be pleased with him, said: "The Prophet, peace and blessings of Allah be upon him, only had their eyes put out because they had put the herdsmen's eyes out," as it says in a report narrated by Muslim.

This narration is quoted as evidence by those who say that camel's urine is *Tahir* (pure), which

is the view of Malik, Ahmad and a number of the *Salaf*. It seems that the Prophet, peace and blessings of Allah be upon him, gave them permission to do that because they were used to it and their bodies were accustomed to it. Their situation was like that of one who is addicted to drugs, who

Camel's Urine

Ammonia	0.05%
Shulphate	0.18%
Phosphate	0.12%
Chloride	0.6%
Magnesium	0.01%
Calcium	0.015%
Potassium	0.6%
Sodium	0.1%
Creatinine	0.1%
Uric acid	0.03%
Urea	2%
Water	95%

may be treated by giving him doses of the drug and gradually reducing them until he is cured of his addiction.

The *Hadith* is to be understood as referring to cases of necessity, like eating dead meat for one who is compelled by necessity to do so. Allah guided some of the professors at the University of Damascus and they made use of this Prophetic medicine in treating a child who had hydrocephalus. The boy's head was very swollen and the doctors were unable to treat it. Then the child's father, who was a knowledgeable believer, remembered the story of the men from 'Uraynah, so he started going to remote areas to collect camel's milk. The outcome was good, rather astonishing, from the first drop of milk swallowed by the child. The benefits of camel's milk and urine may easily be explained by science, because camel's milk contains a large amount of concentrated calcium, as was stated by Dr. Mahmoud Al-Jazeeri, in addition to what Al-Antaki mentioned in his book, which is an important reference work of Arab medicine. He stated that the camel grazes on desert plants such as wormwood and southernwood, which contain substances which open blockages and open vessels, and help to disperse fluids which have collected in cases of oedema or swelling.

(Al-Sunnah Al-Mutahharah Wal-Tahaddiyat)

****

Drinking Water

Al-Bukhari and Muslim narrated from
Anas, may Allah be pleased with him, that
the Messenger of Allah, peace and blessings
of Allah be upon him, used to breathe into
the vessel three times.

It was narrated that Abu Qatadah,
may Allah be pleased with him, said, the
Messenger of Allah, peace and blessings of
Allah be upon him, said: "When one of you
drinks, let him not breathe into the vessel, and
when one of you urinates, let him not touch
his penis with his right hand, and when one
you wipes himself, let him not wipe with his
right hand." (Agreed upon)

Muslim and the authors of *Al-Sunan*
narrated via Abu 'Asim from Anas, may Allah
be pleased with him, that the Prophet, peace
and blessings of Allah be upon him, used
to breathe three times when drinking, and
he would say: "It is more thirst-quenching,
healthier and more wholesome."

What is meant is that it is more enjoyable
and palatable, and more safe from sickness,
thirst or harm.

Some of the scholars said that the
prohibition on breathing into the drink was
like the prohibition of blowing on food and
drink, in the sense that some of the saliva
may fall onto it, so the drinker may be put
off and think it is dirty. This applies if one
is eating and drinking with others, but if a
person is eating on his own or with his family

or people he knows will not be put off, then there is nothing wrong with it.

I say: It is more appropriate to disallow it in all cases, because a person may leave some leftovers, or people may be put off using that vessel and so on. Al-Qurtubi said, "What is meant by the prohibition on breathing into the vessel is so that others will not be put off because of the saliva or because of a bad smell that may reach the water." *Fat'h Al-Bari* 10/94

This is how the earlier scholars understood the *Hadith*. Contemporary scholars have added another meaning. One of them said: This is another example of guidance with which our master Muhammad, peace and blessings of Allah be upon him, has honored us, to protect good manners. Blowing on food and drink is contrary to good manners and makes people look down on and think little of one. The Prophet, peace and blessings of Allah be upon him, is the foremost among the teachers of good manners.

Moreover, breathing involves inhaling and exhaling. Inhaling brings pure, oxygen-rich air into the lungs and

provides the body with what it needs of energy, and exhaling takes out of the lungs air that is rich in carbon dioxide and low in oxygen, along with airborne waste that is expelled from the body via the lungs in gaseous form. The ratio of these gases in exhaled air increases in the case of sickness, as does the level of toxins in the urine. So exhaled air carries gaseous bodily waste and little oxygen, hence the Prophet, peace and blessings of Allah be upon him, forbade blowing onto food and drink.

The Prophet, peace and blessings of Allah be upon him, also pointed to an important principle when he enjoined taking breaths while drinking. It is well-known that the one who drinks in one draught has to hold his breath until he finishes his drink, because the oesophagus and trachea meet at the epiglottis, and they cannot work together at the same time. One of them must stop so that the other can work. When a person holds his breath for a long time, air is detained in the lungs and starts to put pressure on the walls of the alveoli, which expand and gradually lose their flexibility.

The harm that results from that does not appear within a short period, but if a person makes this his habit and drinks water in long draughts like a camel, he will see the symptoms of swollen lungs and will become breathless with little effort, his lips and nails will turn blue, then the pressure of the lungs on the heart will lead to heart failure; it will also be reflected in the liver which will become enlarged, then there will be swelling in all parts of the body. Swelling of the lungs is a serious disease which doctors regard as more serious than lung cancer. The Prophet, peace and blessings of Allah be upon him, did not want the members of his *Ummah* to undergo all this pain and suffering, hence he advised them to sip water and to drink it in three draughts. This is more thirst-quenching, healthier and more wholesome.

(*Al-Haqa'iq Al-Tibbiyah Fil-Islam*)

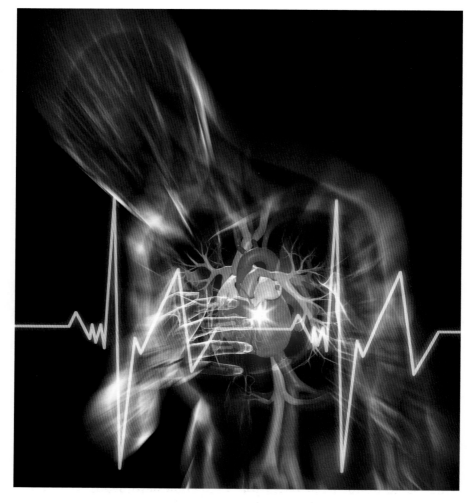

Heart Attack

Hassan Shamsi Pasha

Hardly a minute passes without three people in America experiencing a heart attack, one of whom will meet his end before reaching the hospital and receiving treatment. Heart attacks kill half a million Americans and 150,000 Britons every year. Unfortunately this disease is increasing alarmingly in Arab countries too.

What is a heart attack (myocardial infarction)?

A heart attack is the result of a blockage in one of the coronary arteries, which leads to death of the part of the heart muscle that was supplied by that blood vessel. At that stage the patient complains of severe pain in the chest, accompanied by sweating and nausea.

Angina (full name: *Angina pectoris*) is pain in the middle of the chest resulting from exertion, which usually goes away when the exertion stops. It results from narrowing (not blockage) of the coronary arteries.

What are the factors that lead to disease of the blood vessels of the heart?

The factors that may lead to this disease may be divided into those which are beyond one's control, such as age, gender and heredity; and those which one is able to control, such as smoking, high cholesterol, high blood pressure, diabetes, obesity, lack of exercise and psychological pressure. It is possible to protect oneself against this disease by taking charge of the latter group of factors or avoiding them.

The teachings of the Prophet, peace and blessings of Allah be upon him, protect against heart attacks:

• Avoiding high cholesterol and obesity

High cholesterol usually results from eating too much animal fat such as meat, cream, butter, cheese, *ghee* (clarified butter) and so on. There may also be a family predisposition toward high cholesterol. There is no doubt whatsoever that high cholesterol leads to a higher risk of coronary heart disease.

Obesity may lead to diabetes and high blood pressure, as well as coronary heart disease, especially in middle aged men. We know that obesity usually results from overeating and lack of an active lifestyle. Nutrition experts now advise eating food that is low in saturated fat and cholesterol and maintaining an ideal body weight.

How can that be done? The Messenger of Allah, peace and blessings of Allah be upon him, encouraged moderation in eating and avoiding overeating. At-Tirmidhi narrated with a *hasan isnad* that Ibn 'Umar

said, "A man burped in the presence of the Prophet, peace and blessings of Allah be upon him, and he said: 'Keep your burps away from us, for those who filled their stomachs the most in this world will be hungry the longest on the Day of Resurrection'."

And it was narrated that 'A'ishah, may Allah be pleased with her, said: "The first problem that arose in this Ummah after their Prophet passed away came after they started to eat their

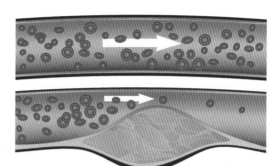
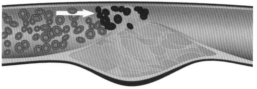

Cholesterol plaque in artery (atherosclerosis) illustration. Top artery is healthy. Middle & bottom arteries show plaque formation, rupturing, clotting & blood flow occlusion

fill. When people fill their bellies their bodies get fat and their hearts grow weak (spiritually) and their desires become strong." (Narrated by Al-Bukhari in *Kitab Ad-Du'afa*, and by Ibn Abi Dunya)

If we want to avoid obesity and the dangers that it poses to the heart, lungs and gallbladder, and avoid the risk of diabetes, all we have to do is remember and apply the words of the Messenger of Allah, peace and blessings of Allah be upon him, at every meal: "The son of Adam does not fill any vessel worse than his stomach. It is sufficient for the son of Adam to eat a few mouthfuls to give him enough strength. If his desire for food overwhelms him, then let him fill one-third with food, one-third with drink and leave one-third for air." (*Saheeh*; narrated by Ahmad and Al-Tirmidhi)

Allah, Most High, has mentioned health and nutrition in a few words in one Verse. He says:

$$ \text{﴿ وَكُلُواْ وَٱشْرَبُواْ وَلَا تُسْرِفُوٓاْ إِنَّهُۥ لَا يُحِبُّ ٱلْمُسْرِفِينَ ﴾} $$

"And eat and drink but waste not by extravagance, certainly He (Allah) likes not Al-Musrifoon (those who waste by extravagance)." (Soorah Al-A'raf, 7:31)

- ## Eating olive oil & Fish oil

Recent scientific studies have proved the benefit of olive oil in reducing cholesterol, and studies have shown that Mediterranean countries have the lowest incidence of coronary heart disease because their inhabitants eat a great deal of olive oil.

This oil is what the Messenger of Allah, peace and blessings of Allah be upon him, advised us to eat, when he said: "Eat (olive) oil and apply it to your skin, for it comes from a blessed tree." (Ahmad and Al-Tirmidhi; *Saheeh*) It is a tree which Allah mentioned in the Qur'an, when He said:

﴿ يُوقَدُ مِن شَجَرَةٍ مُّبَـٰرَكَةٍ زَيْتُونَةٍ لَّا شَرْقِيَّةٍ وَلَا غَرْبِيَّةٍ ﴾

"Lit from a blessed tree, an olive, neither of the East (i.e. neither it gets sunrays only in the morning) nor of the West (i.e. nor it gets sunrays only in the afternoon, but it is exposed to the sun all day long)." (Soorah Al-Noor, 24:35)

Nutrition experts and cardiologists worldwide recommend eating at least two meals of fish per week. The Prophet, peace and blessings of Allah be upon him, drew attention to the benefits of fish when he said: "The first food of the people of Paradise will be oil from fish liver." (Narrated by Muslim)

The fish oil which doctors recommend as a remedy for high triglyceride levels (triglyceride is one of the fats in the blood) is derived from the liver of the fish. Eating fish is not only beneficial in protecting oneself against coronary artery disease and high levels of fat in the blood, it also has other benefits in treating migraines, joint pain and many other problems.

• Physical exercise

It has now been confirmed through extensive research that in order to protect oneself against coronary heart disease and heart attacks, it is essential to do some form of physical exercise such as brisk walking, running or swimming for twenty minutes two or three times a week at least.

To these people we say that the Messenger of Allah, peace and blessings of Allah be upon him, encouraged us to walk to the mosque not just two or three times a week, rather five times in one day, and the mosque may be ten minutes away or more.

Is this not an exercise for the body and protection for the heart? Al-Bukhari and Muslim narrated in their *Saheehain* that the Messenger of Allah, peace and blessings of Allah be upon him, said: "The one who will be given the greatest reward for prayer will be the one who has to walk the furthest, then the next furthest. The one who waits for the prayer until he prays it with the *Imam* will have a greater reward than the one who prays then sleeps."

According to another report: "… until he prays it with the Imam in congregation."

Doctors confirm the importance of the walking being brisk and energetic, not slow and easy. Is this not the walk of a true Muslim who follows the example of the Messenger of Allah, peace and blessings of Allah be upon him, in all his actions?

Ibn Al-Qayyim, may Allah have mercy on him, said, "When the Messenger of Allah, peace and blessings of Allah be upon him, walked, he leaned forward and he was the quickest of people in walking."

Muslim narrated that Anas, may Allah be pleased with him, said:

"The Messenger of Allah, peace and blessings of Allah be upon him, was of a fair complexion, and his sweat was like pearls. When he walked, he leaned forward. May the blessings and peace of Allah be upon him."

• Refraining from smoking

Scientific studies have definitively established that the risk of heart disease among smokers is three times greater than among non-smokers. It is no secret to anyone that smoking is harmful to the heart, lungs and other organs in the body.

A number of jurists have stated that smoking is *Haram*, based on the narration of the Messenger of Allah, peace and blessings of Allah be upon him: "There should be neither harming nor reciprocating harm." (Narrated by Ahmad; it is a *saheeh Hadith*)

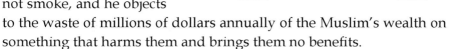

The true Muslim does not smoke, and he objects to the waste of millions of dollars annually of the Muslim's wealth on something that harms them and brings them no benefits.

• Treating high blood pressure and diabetes

It is certain that controlling high blood pressure and treating diabetes play a role in protecting against heart disease. The Messenger of Allah, peace and blessings of Allah be upon him, enjoined using medicine when he said:

"Treat sickness, O slaves of Allah, for Allah has not sent down any disease but He has sent down a cure for it, except one disease – old age." (Narrated by Ahmad and the four; classed as *saheeh* by Al-Tirmidhi)

- ## Dealing with psychological pressure

Scientific studies have confirmed that exposure to psychological stress, distress or strong emotions may provoke an attack of angina. There is recent scientific evidence which suggests that those who get very angry are most at risk of coronary heart disease. We all know the famous narration of the Messenger of Allah, peace and blessings of Allah be upon him, in which he advised a man who came to him and asked him, O Messenger of Allah, advise me. The Prophet, peace and blessings of Allah be upon him: "Do not get angry." (Narrated by Al-Bukhari)

And he said: "If one of you gets angry and he is standing, let him

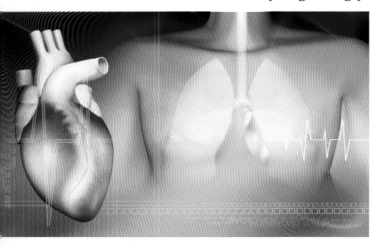

sit down, and if his anger goes away (all well and good), otherwise let him lie down." (Narrated by Ahmad; it is a *saheeh Hadith*)

Islam teaches us to be patient in the face of hardships and calamity. In the *Saheeh Hadith* narrated by Muslim, the Prophet, peace and blessings of Allah be upon him, said: "How wonderful is the affair of the believer, for all his affairs are good, and that is for no one except the believer. If something good happens to him, he gives thanks, and that is good for him, and if something bad happens to him, he bears it with patience and that is good for him."

How can the Muslim not submit all his affairs to the Creator of the heavens and the Earth?

*****

Chapter: 29

Cauterization

Dr. Muhammad Bakr Isma'eel
Professor at the University of Cairo

Question: I have read in the books of *Hadith* that cauterization with fire is a remedy for many diseases. The Messenger (peace and blessings of Allah be upon him) mentioned it among the remedies with which the sick are treated, but I also read in these books that the Messenger, peace and blessings of Allah be upon him, forbade it and said: "I do not use cauterization."

But I have also read that he treated others by this means. I checked some books of *Fiqh* (Islamic jurisprudence) and I found out that the *Fuqaha'* (jurists) differed concerning the ruling on cautery. Some of the~ said it is permitted and some forbade it, and some said it is M (discouraged in Islam). Which of these opinions is most co~ can we reconcile between these reports?

Dr. Muhammad Bakr Isma'eel replied: In the name

be to Allah, and blessings and peace be upon the Messenger of Allah.

Cautery is a specific kind of medicine that may be needed in some cases, but it is not a regular kind of medicine. The Messenger, peace and blessings of Allah be upon him, disliked it but he did not forbid it. The use of cauterization as a remedy depends on the prescription of a trustworthy doctor, but it should be a last resort.

The reader may sometimes find in the books of *Sunnah* some *Ahadeeth* (narrations) that seem to contradict one another, so the reader who has little knowledge becomes confused and hesitant concerning the ruling on the issue that he wants to find out about. If he is lucky he will ask scholars who have a proper understanding of Islamic jurisprudence and they will give him a clear and satisfying answer. Hence, Allah, the Exalted, told the one who has no knowledge of a thing and wants to know the ruling in *Shari'ah* on it to ask the people of knowledge. He says in His Book:

$$ ﴿ فَسْـَٔلُوٓاْ أَهْلَ ٱلذِّكْرِ إِن كُنتُمْ لَا تَعْلَمُونَ ﴾ $$

"So ask the people of the Reminder if you do not know." (Soorahs Al-Nahl & Al-Anbiya', 21:7)

Knowledge has locked doors, the key to which is asking.

Before answering this question, we want to tell you that you should know that when there seem to be contradictions between narrations of the Prophet, peace and blessings of Allah be upon him, we say:

- You should first enquire closely as to the soundness of these narrations. If you find that one is *Saheeh* (sound) and the other is *Dha'eef* (weak), then you must give precedence to the one that is sound over the one that is weak, and base the ruling on it, and overlook the report that is weak or less sound. So the sound takes precedence over the weak, and the more sound takes precedence over the sound. This way of judging is the way of the scholars, when there are conflicting reports.

- If you find that the narrations are all at the same level of soundness, you have to connect each narration to a specific case or time as much as you can, unless you know that some are

abrogated by others. If you know which abrogated (the other narration) and which was abrogated, then there is no conflict, as the ruling in the abrogated report is superseded by the ruling that abrogated it.

• If you find that the narrations are all sound and you do not know which abrogated and which was abrogated, and you cannot reconcile between them, then refrain from deriving any ruling from them and do your best to research and study the matter. Ask scholars and seek the help of Allah, the Exalted, to find out the ruling from all of them on an equal basis as much as possible. I would like to reassure you that there is nothing contradictory in the Book of Allah or the *Sunnah* of the Messenger of Allah, peace and blessings of Allah be upon him, praise be to Allah.

I hope that this brief introduction will be beneficial to you with regard to all matters in which you think there are contradictions.

Now I would like to answer your question. There are narrations which say that cauterization is a medicine, but it is a last resort, in the sense that it should not be resorted to unless the case is urgent and there is no other remedy. It was narrated in *Saheeh Al-Bukhari*

that Jabir Ibn 'Abdullah, may Allah be pleased with him, said, I heard the Prophet, peace and blessings of Allah be upon him, say: "If there is anything good in your medicine, then it is in the instrument of a cupper, drinking honey or the touch of fire suited to the disease, but I would not like to be cauterized."

The words "suited to the disease" indicate that using cauterization is not allowed if there is something else that can be used instead.

The words "I would not like to be cauterized" indicate that he disliked it, not that it is *Makrooh* in and of itself. In *Saheeh Muslim* it is narrated that Jabir Ibn 'Abdullah, may Allah be pleased with him, said: "Sa'd Ibn Mu'adh was wounded in his medial arm vein, and the Prophet, peace and blessings of Allah be upon him, cauterized it with his own hand, using an iron arrowhead. Then it swelled up and he cauterized it again – i.e., he stopped the bleeding from the vein using cautery – with an arrow that he had in his hand."

It also says in *Saheeh Muslim* that the Prophet, peace and blessings of Allah be upon him, sent a doctor to Ubayy Ibn Ka'b, may Allah be pleased with him, and he cut a vein then he cauterized it.

And there are narrations which forbid cauterizing, such as the report narrated by Al-Bukhari in his *Saheeh* from Ibn 'Abbas, may Allah be pleased with him, who said that the Prophet, peace and blessings of Allah be upon him, said: "Healing is in three things: drinking honey, the instrument of a cupper, and cauterization with fire, but I do not allow my *Ummah* to use cauterization."

Al-Bukhari said that the *Hadith* is *marfoo'*, i.e., Ibn 'Abbas attributed it to the Prophet, peace and blessings of Allah be upon him, on the basis of the words "but I do not allow my *Ummah* to use cauterization."

Ahmad, Abu Dawood and Al-Tirmidhi narrated that 'Imran Ibn Husain, may Allah be pleased with him, said: "The Messenger of Allah, peace and blessings of Allah be upon him, did not allow cauterization. We used cauterization but we never succeeded or prospered."

These narrations may be reconciled if we note that cauterization is permissible in cases of necessity when there is no other alternative, so long as it is prescribed by a proficient Muslim doctor. It is *Haram* for the one who has another option and can do without it, and it is *Makrooh* if

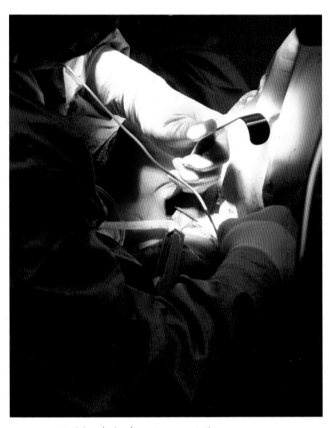
surgeon couterizing during breast augmentation

the person has no problem that forces him to resort to it, such as a healthy person who fears that some problem could befall him, so he uses cauterization before the problem arises, because this is contrary to *Tawakkul* (putting one's trust in Allah). But if there is widespread disease and doctors think that cauterization may protect against it, then it is permissible for them to use cautery and it is not *Makrooh*, because prevention is better than cure.

Based on this, we can understand the *Hadith* which was narrated by Al-Bukhari in his *Saheeh*, about people who will be admitted to Paradise without reckoning. The Prophet, peace and blessings of Allah be upon him, said, describing them: "They are the ones who did not ask others to do *Ruqyah* for them, or believe in omens, or use cauterization, and they put their trust in their Lord," i.e., they did not ask for *Ruqyah* as some other people ask the righteous among them, and they were not superstitious, and they did not cauterize with fire, out of trust in Allah. They are the elite and we cannot compare ourselves with them.

Or it may be understood as referring to one who is healthy but fears disease because of some worries or illusions that he has, because this

worry is a sort of sickness that is contrary to *Tawakkul*, and *Tawakkul* is one of the fruits of faith. Those people are among the elite based on the fact that they will enter Paradise without being brought to account.

Moreover, in the past, cauterization was a primitive remedy that was done by people who had experience of the best way to do it and knowledge of the diseases that could be treated with it. They were treating sickness with what was available to them on the basis of the medical knowledge that they had. But medicine has developed greatly and has progressed in all fields, and the use of cautery has naturally developed likewise. Precise equipment has been invented for it that uses electricity. But despite that the ruling has not changed. Cauterization with any newly developed instrument or in any way is only to be used when there is no alternative.

I liked what An-Nawawi, may Allah have Mercy upon him, said concerning medicine and the remedies used by doctors. He said in *Sharh Muslim*: The science of medicine is most in need of detailed explanation, because the sick person may be using something as a remedy at one stage, but at another stage the same remedy becomes problematic for him, so that what was the cure at one time will become a disease at another, due to some change of mood or environment, such as anger, a change of climate or other countless things. So when the cure is found for a particular individual at a certain stage, it does not necessarily mean that this remedy will be good at other stages or for all other people. Doctors agree that one sickness may have many remedies, according to age, time, habits, diet and the individual's strength.

We ask Allah, the Exalted, for guidance. And Allah knows best.

*****

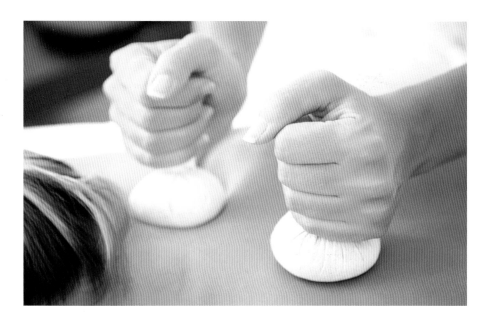

Application of Hot Compresses

It was narrated that 'A'ishah, may Allah be pleased with her, said, the Messenger of Allah, peace and blessings of Allah be upon him, said: "Instead of cauterizing use hot compresses; instead of squeezing the uvula of a child with a sore throat, use drops in the nose; instead of blowing, use medicine administered through the side of the mouth." (Narrated by Ahmad; the men of its *Isnad* are the men of *Saheeh*, except that its *Isnad* includes Ibrahim Al-Nakha'i who did not hear from 'A'ishah, may Allah be pleased with her, but the fact that he did not hear does not matter because his *mursal* reports are *Saheeh* according to scholars of *Hadith*.)

It was narrated that Ibn Mas'ood, may Allah be pleased with him, said, some people came to the Prophet, peace and blessings of Allah be upon him, and said, "O Messenger of Allah, one of our companions

is sick; should we cauterize him?" He remained silent for a moment and then he said: "If you wish you may cauterize him, and if you wish you may use heated stones." (Narrated by Ahmad; Al-Haithami said: Its men are *Thiqat* (t r u s t w o r t h y) except that Abu 'Ubaidah did not hear from his father. But Al-Bukhari narrated in *Kitab Al-Kuna* that he may have heard from his father.)

Most of the Arabs during the *Jahiliyyah* (pre-Islamic era of ignorance) used cauterization quite frequently, especially in the treatment of pain. But Islam forbade cauterization except when used properly by those who had experience in this skill, and the Prophet, peace and blessings of Allah be upon him, suggested an alternative means of physical treatment aimed at alleviating pain which offered great benefits, namely the use of hot compresses. Use of hot compresses involves warming the affected body part by wrapping it in a heated cloth. Even today, folk medicine still uses this method to treat stomach pain and some other kinds of pain, especially those that occur as the result of exposure to cold, by applying a heated towel, or a heated stone or clay which is first wrapped in a cloth so as to avoid causing burns to the skin.

Modern medicine uses hot compresses to fight pain, using a cloth wetted with water that has been heated to a bearable temperature and to which some medicines may be added. Hot compresses are prepared by dipping a folded towel or piece of soft 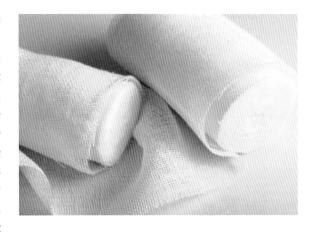 gauze into hot water, then wrapping it around the area to be treated, be it the chest, abdomen or a limb. Some wax, rubber or nylon may be placed over it, then it may be wrapped with a bandage to keep it in place. Hot compresses are beneficial in treating congestion of the lungs and trachea, stomach and pelvic pain, and adhesions resulting from infection or surgery. They also help to draw out pus in the case of abscesses and boils, thus reducing the pain and confining the pus to the abscess, which helps to draw it out or facilitates lancing thereof.

(Dr. Mahmoud Nazim Al-Naseemi, *Al-Tibb An-Nabawi Wal-'Ilm Al-Hadith*)

✳✳✳✳✳

Protection

It was narrated that Jabir Ibn 'Abdullah, may Allah be pleased with him, said, I heard the Messenger of Allah, peace and blessings Allah be upon him, say: "Cover the vessels and tie up the water skins, for there is one night in the year when pestilence descends, and it does not pass by any vessel that is not covered or any water skin that is not tied up, but some of that pestilence descends into it." (Narrated by Muslim) At the end of the *Hadith* he adds, Al-Laith said, "The non-Arabs among us protect themselves against that in *Kanoon Al-Awwal*." (December)

Modern medicine has proved that the Prophet, peace and blessings of Allah be upon him, was the first one to lay down the principles of protecting health by taking precautions against contagious disease. It has become apparent that contagious diseases spread at certain times of the year, and some of them appear at regular intervals every few years, according to a precise system that was not

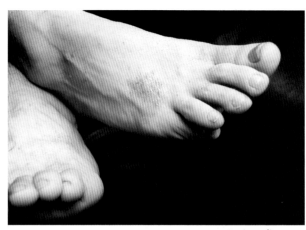

contagious diseases

known until today. For example, measles and polio are more widespread in September and October, typhoid is more prevalent in summer, and cholera appears every seven years.

This shows us the scientific miracle in the words of the Prophet, peace and blessings of Allah be upon him: "For there is one night in the year when pestilence descends", i.e., a seasonal epidemic which appears at certain times."

One of the scientific facts that were not known until after the invention of the microscope is that some contagious diseases are transmitted through the air via water vapor and dust, which is what is referred to in the *Hadith* (narration). The germs cling to dust particles when they are carried by the wind, and thus travel from the sick person to a healthy one. Who told the Messenger of Allah, peace and blessings of Allah be upon him, about all this? Was it not Allah, may He be Exalted?